MATHS

FOR ADVANCED PHYSICS

Andrew Lambert

Nelson

Thomas Nelson and Sons Ltd
Nelson House Mayfield Road
Walton-on-Thames Surrey
KT12 5PL UK

Nelson Blackie
Wester Cleddens Road
Bishopbriggs
Glasgow
G64 2NZ UK

Thomas Nelson Australia
102 Dodds Street
South Melbourne
Victoria 3205 Australia

Nelson Canada
1120 Birchmount Road
Scarborough Ontario
M1K 5G4 Canada

First published by Thomas Nelson and Sons Ltd 1993

I(T)P Thomas Nelson is an International
    Thomson Publishing Company.

I(T)P is used under licence.

ISBN 0-17-448213-2
NPN 9 8 7 6 5 4 3

Printed in Great Britain by Hobbs the Printers of Southampton

Contents

1 *Manipulating Equations*

1.1 INTRODUCTION

Physicists are often concerned with the **relationships** between quantities and the way in which one quantity changes as another is altered. Relationships could be written out in words, for example:

force is equal to mass multiplied by acceleration

but for conciseness these relationships are usually written as an algebraic equation, with one letter to represent each quantity, for example

$$F = ma$$

Even quite simple relationships would be quite difficult to follow if they were not written in this way, for example, compare

distance travelled is equal to initial velocity multiplied by time taken plus one half of the acceleration multiplied by the square of the time taken

with

$$s = ut + \tfrac{1}{2}at^2$$

Apart from conciseness, equations have the advantage that they can easily be manipulated using the rules of algebra, which is often necessary to help solve problems.

1.2 SIGNS AND SYMBOLS

In order to understand the language of algebra and arithmetic, you need to know the symbols listed in Table 1.1. The meaning of some of these symbols will made clearer in later chapters, but all the necessary signs and symbols are included here for convenience.

Table 1.1 Algebraic symbols

Symbol	Meaning	Example	
$<$	less than	$x < 20$	x is less than 20
$>$	greater than	$y > 15$	y is greater than 15
$\ll$	much less than	$z \ll 1$	z is much less than 1
$\gg$	much greater than	$w \gg 5$	w is much greater than 5
$\leqslant$	less than or equal to	$x \leqslant 1$	x is less than or equal to 1
$\geqslant$	greater than or equal to	$y \geqslant 1$	y is greater than or equal to 1
$=$	equal to	$w = 5$	w has a value of 5
$\approx$	approximately equal to	$\pi^2 \approx 10$	π^2 is approximately equal to 10
$\neq$	not equal to	$z \neq a$	z does not equal a
$\propto$	proportional to	$F \propto a$	F is proportional to a
$\bar{x}$	mean or average	$\bar{x} = 6$	the mean value of x is 6

1.3 THE BASIC RULES OF ALGEBRA AND ARITHMETIC

In order to be able to manipulate algebraic equations as well as carrying out numerical calculations, you must know and understand the basic rules of algebra. Four useful examples are shown in Table 1.2.

Table 1.2 Simple algebraic rules

	Example
$by = y + y + ...$(b times)	$3y = y + y + y$
$ay + by = (a + b)y$	$2y + 3y = 5y$
$\dfrac{1}{\left(\frac{a}{y}\right)} = \dfrac{y}{a}$	$\dfrac{1}{\left(\frac{2}{y}\right)} = \dfrac{y}{2}$
$\dfrac{\left(\frac{b}{z}\right)}{\left(\frac{a}{y}\right)} = \dfrac{by}{az}$	$\dfrac{\left(\frac{3}{z}\right)}{\left(\frac{2}{y}\right)} = \dfrac{3y}{2z}$

1.4 HANDLING INDICES

y^a means y multiplied by itself a times. For example, 4^3 means $4 \times 4 \times 4 = 64$.

a is called the **index**, or the **power** to which y is raised. (We say, for example 'y to the power of a' or '4 to the power of 3'.)

Many scientific equations contain indices. The rules for manipulating indices are shown in Table 1.3.

Table 1.3 Handling indices

	Algebraic example	Numerical example
$y^{-n} = \dfrac{1}{y^n}$	$y^{-3} = \dfrac{1}{y^3}$	$4^{-3} = \dfrac{1}{4^3} = \dfrac{1}{64} = 0.0156$
$y^{\frac{1}{a}} = \sqrt[a]{y}$	$y^{\frac{1}{2}} = \sqrt{y}$	$4^{\frac{1}{2}} = \sqrt{4} = 2$
$y^a + y^b$ cannot be simplified		$4^2 + 4^3 = 16 + 64 = 80$
$y^a \times y^b = y^{a+b}$	$y^2 \times y^3 = y^5$	$4^2 \times 4^3 = 4^5 = 1024$
$\dfrac{y^a}{y^b} = y^{a-b}$	$\dfrac{y^2}{y^3} = y^{2-3} = y^{-1}$	$\dfrac{4^2}{4^3} = 4^{-1} = \dfrac{1}{4} = 0.25$
$\left(y^a\right)^b = y^{a\times b}$	$\left(y^2\right)^3 = y^6$	$\left(4^2\right)^3 = 4^6 = 4096$
$y^{\frac{b}{a}} = \sqrt[a]{y^b}$	$y^{\frac{3}{2}} = \sqrt[2]{y^3}$	$4^{\frac{3}{2}} = \sqrt[2]{4^3} = 8$
$y^0 = 1$		$4^0 = 1$

✍ **Student task 1.1**

a) Simplify the following:

i) $y^6 \times y^7$

ii) $y^8 \div y^5$

iii) $(y^3)^4$

iv) $3y^2 \times 4y^3$

b) Calculate the values of the following:

i) 3^4

ii) $8^{\frac{1}{3}}$

iii) 5^{-2}

iv) $9^{\frac{3}{2}}$

v) $16^{-\frac{1}{2}}$

vi) 6^0

1.5 CHANGING THE SUBJECT OF AN EQUATION

In the equation $v = u + at$, v is known as the **subject** of the equation. You can calculate a value for v if you know the values of u, a and t by substituting these values into the equation. However, you may need to calculate the value of t, for example, so you would need to make t the subject of the equation.

Changing the subject of an equation is based on the general principle:

> **Whatever change you make to one side of the equation, you must make the same change to the other side.**

The following examples should make this clear.

i) Addition and subtraction

The equation for resistors in series is:

$$R_T = R_1 + R_2$$

To make R_1 the subject of the equation, we subtract R_2 from the right hand-side, leaving only R_1, so we also subtract R_2 from the left-hand side, giving:

$$R_T - R_2 = R_1$$

or

$$R_1 = R_T - R_2$$

Effectively, we have moved R_2 to the other side of the equation and changed its sign from positive to negative.

> **If something which is added to one side of an equation is moved to the other side, it changes its sign from positive to negative. Conversely, if something which is subtracted from one side of an equation is moved to the other side, it changes its sign from negative to positive.**

> ✍ *Student task 1.2*
>
> a) Make u the subject of $v = u + at$
>
> b) Make E_k the subject of $hf = \varphi + E_k$
>
> c) Make $\frac{1}{v}$ the subject of $\frac{1}{u} + \frac{1}{v} = \frac{1}{f}$

ii) Multiplication and division

This is by far the most common kind of equation in Physics.

The equation for power in an electric circuit is:

$$P = VI$$

To make V the subject of the equation, we divide the right hand side by I, so we must also divide the left hand side by I giving:

$$\frac{P}{I} = V$$

Effectively we have moved I to the other side of the equation and changed its sign from 'multiply' to 'divide'.

> **If something which multiplies one side of an equation is moved to the other side, it divides that side of the equation (it moves from being a *numerator* to being a *denominator*). Conversely, if something which divides one side of an equation moves to the other side, it multiplies that side of the equation.**

> ✍ *Student task 1.3*
>
> a) Make B the subject of $F = BIl$
>
> b) Make ρ the subject of $R = \dfrac{\rho l}{A}$
>
> c) Make V the subject of $C = \dfrac{Q}{V}$

iii) Squares and square roots

If $x^2 = a + b$

then to find x we must find the **square root** of both sides, so

$$x = \sqrt{a + b}$$

If $\sqrt{y} = c + d$

then to find y we must **square** both sides, so

$$y = (c + d)^2$$

iv) Further examples

Example a)

The efficiency of a heat engine is given by the equation:

$$E = \frac{T_1 - T_2}{T_1}$$

Make T_2 the subject of the equation.

Since the whole of the right-hand side of the equation is divided by T_1, the first step is to take this T_1 to the left-hand side:

$$ET_1 = T_1 - T_2$$

Now $-T_2$ can be taken to the left, and ET_1 to the right:

$$T_2 = T_1 - ET_1$$

Finally, T_1 could be taken out as a common factor on the right:

$$T_2 = T_1 (1 - E)$$

If we wanted to make T_1 the subject of the equation, we would have to go through the same steps, and finally take the $(1 - E)$ to the left-hand side, leaving just T_1 on the right:

$$\frac{T_2}{(1 - E)} = T_1$$

✳ Pitfall 1.1

In this example, it is easy to forget that T_2 is divided by T_1, resulting in the following:

$$E = \frac{T_1 - T_2}{T_1} \quad \Longrightarrow \quad E + T_2 = \frac{T_1}{T_1} = 1$$

which is clearly nonsense!

Example b)

The frequency of oscillation of a mass on a spring is given by:

$$f = \frac{1}{2\pi}\sqrt{\frac{k}{m}}$$

Make k the subject of the equation.

Since m is inside the square root sign, we start by moving 2π to the left-hand side:

$$f = \frac{1}{2\pi}\sqrt{\frac{k}{m}} \quad \Longrightarrow \quad 2\pi f = \sqrt{\frac{k}{m}}$$

Now both sides of the equation can be squared to remove the square root:

$$2\pi f = \sqrt{\frac{k}{m}} \quad \Longrightarrow \quad (2\pi f)^2 = \frac{k}{m}$$

Finally, m can be moved to the opposite side of the equation.

$$(2\pi f)^2 = \frac{k}{m} \quad \Longrightarrow \quad m(2\pi f)^2 = k$$

✳ Pitfall 1.2

Beware of accidentally removing a variable from within a square root. A possible mistake in the previous example is:

$$f = \frac{1}{2\pi}\sqrt{\frac{k}{m}} \quad \Longrightarrow \quad mf = \frac{1}{2\pi}\sqrt{k}$$

However, the following is correct, although not particularly easy to work with:

$$f = \frac{1}{2\pi}\sqrt{\frac{k}{m}} \quad \Longrightarrow \quad \sqrt{m}\, f = \frac{1}{2\pi}\sqrt{k}$$

However, it is possible to confuse the following:

$$\sqrt{m}\, f \quad \text{with} \quad \sqrt{mf}$$

especially with hasty handwriting. It is much safer to write this as:

$$f\sqrt{m}$$

Example c)

Make u the subject of the following equation of motion:

$$v^2 = u^2 + 2as$$

The necessary stages are:

$$v^2 = u^2 + 2as \quad \Longrightarrow \quad u^2 = v^2 - 2as$$

$$u^2 = v^2 - 2as \quad \Longrightarrow \quad u = \sqrt{v^2 - 2as}$$

✳ Pitfall 1.3

$\sqrt{v^2 - 2as}$ does not equal $v - \sqrt{2as}$

5

Example d)

It is often necessary to move several variables to achieve what is required, but the principles remain the same.

The magnetic field in a long solenoid is given by:

$$B = \frac{\mu_0 NI}{l}$$

To make I the subject of the equation, we move l to the left, where it becomes part of the numerator ('from the bottom to the top of the fraction'), while $\mu_0 N$ moves to the left to become part of the denominator ('from the top to the bottom of the fraction'), giving:

$$\frac{Bl}{\mu_0 N} = I \quad \text{or} \quad I = \frac{Bl}{\mu_0 N}$$

✍ Student task 1.4

a) Make l the subject of $\quad R = \dfrac{\rho l}{A}$

b) Make x the subject of $\quad \dfrac{\lambda}{x} = \dfrac{s}{l}$

c) Make v the subject of $\quad F = \dfrac{mv^2}{r}$

d) Make r the subject of $\quad F = \dfrac{Gm_1 m_2}{r^2}$

e) Make E the subject of $\quad c = \sqrt{\dfrac{E}{\rho}}$

f) Make T the subject of $\quad f = 2\pi\sqrt{\dfrac{T}{\mu}}$

g) Make L the subject of $\quad f_r = \dfrac{1}{2\pi\sqrt{LC}}$

1.6 SIMULTANEOUS EQUATIONS

If you have two equations relating two different unknown quantities, these equations are known as 'simultaneous'. They have a limited use in A-level Physics.

A simple example of a pair of simultaneous equations is:

$$x + 7y = 38$$
$$x + 3y = 18$$

To solve these equations (that is, find the values of x and y), we need to eliminate one of the variables; in this case it is easiest to eliminate x by subtracting the second equation from the first:

$$x + 7y = 38$$
$$\underline{x + 3y = 18}$$
$$(x - x) + (7y - 3y) = (38 - 18)$$
$$4y = 20$$
$$\therefore y = 5$$

This value for y can now be substituted back into the first of the pair of equations to find a value for x:

$$x + (7 \times 5) = 38$$
$$x + 35 = 38$$
$$\therefore x = 3$$

Example

Two cars are moving along a road; car 1 is moving at a steady speed of 20 m/s; car 2 is 150 m in front of car 1 and moving at a steady speed of 15 m/s.

How much time passes before car 1 catches up with car 2, and how far will it have travelled?

Let s be the displacement when they meet, measured from the starting position of the first car, v_1 and v_2 the respective speeds of the cars and t the time at which they meet.

For car 1: $s = v_1 t$ $\therefore s = 20t$

For car 2: $s = v_2 t + 150$ $\therefore s = 15t + 150$

Subtracting the two equations gives:

$$0 = 5t - 150$$
$$5t = 150$$
$$\therefore t = 30$$

Car 1 passes car 2 after 30 seconds.

By substituting this value into the first equation, we can see that car 1 travels

$$20 \text{ m/s} \times 30 \text{ s} = 600 \text{ m}$$

before overtaking car 2.

An equation which contains both x^2 and x is known as a quadratic equation. Quadratic equations do not occur very often in A-level Physics.

The general form of a quadratic equation is:

$$ax^2 + bx + c = 0$$

where x is a variable and a, b and c are constants.

The general solution to this equation is:

$$x = \frac{-b \pm \sqrt{b^2 - 4ac}}{2a}$$

Notice that there will usually be two possible values for x.

A simple example of a quadratic equation is:

$$2x^2 - 11x + 4 = 0$$

Here a = 2, b = -11 and c = 4.

The two possible values of x are given by:

$$x = \frac{11 \pm \sqrt{121 - 32}}{4}$$

$$\therefore x = \frac{11 + \sqrt{89}}{4} \quad \text{or} \quad \frac{11 - \sqrt{89}}{4}$$

Hence $x = 5.11$ or $x = 0.39$

(You may be aware of another method of solving quadratic equations involving factorisation. The figures involved in the real world of Physics rarely make this method feasible).

The most common quadratic equation to occur in A-level Physics is the equation of motion $s = ut + \frac{1}{2}at^2$.

Example

A ball is launched vertically upwards with a speed of 150 m/s. How much time elapses before it reaches a height of 500 m?

Table of information:

initial speed $u = 150$ m/s
acceleration $a = -10$ m/s^2
displacement $s = 500$ m

(Note: if the initial velocity is positive, the acceleration is negative since it is in the opposite direction.)

Calculation:

Using

$$s = ut + \frac{1}{2}at^2$$
$$500 = 150t - (\frac{1}{2} \times 10t^2)$$
$$500 = 150t - 5t^2$$

Rearranging the equation:

$$5t^2 - 150t + 500 = 0$$

and dividing all through by 5:

$$t^2 - 30t + 100 = 0$$

Using the general equation to find the values of t:

$$t = \frac{-(-30) \pm \sqrt{900 - 400}}{2}$$

$$t = \frac{30 + \sqrt{500}}{2} \quad \text{or} \quad t = \frac{30 - \sqrt{500}}{2}$$

$$\therefore t = 26.2 \text{ or } 3.8$$

The time taken is either 3.8 s or 26.2 s. The first value is the time taken to pass the 500 m height on the way up, and the second the time to pass on the way down. A little thought about the situation is needed to interpret the Mathematics.

✱ *Pitfall 1.4*

Beware of meaningless negative answers to quadratic equations. For example:

A ball is thrown down with an initial velocity of 15 m/s from a tower 60 m tall. How much time elapses before it hits the ground?

A similar calculation to the previous example using these figures gives times of 2.3 s or -5.3 s. The second answer is nonsense in this context.

✐ *Student task 1.5*

a)   Solve the problem in Pitfall 1.4 to satisfy yourself that the times quoted are correct.

b)   Can you think of what the -5.3 s obtained as the second answer in this example could represent?

1.8 DEDUCTIONS FROM EQUATIONS

This section is concerned with the effect on one variable of changing another related variable, as in the following examples.

Example 1

$$F = ma$$

If the force F doubles and the mass m remains constant, then the acceleration a must double as well for the equation to remain balanced. If the value of the left-hand side of an equation doubles, then the value of the right-hand side must also double.

Similarly, if F trebles, a trebles; if F halves, a halves, and so on. We say that F and a are **directly proportional** to each other.

Example 2

$$stress = \frac{force}{area}$$

If the *area* doubles and the force remains constant, the value of the right-hand side halves, since the *force* is divided by a number twice as large as before. Therefore the value of *stress* halves.

Here we say that the *stress* and *area* are **inversely proportional** to each other.

Example 3

The equation relating the period T of a pendulum to its length l is given by:

$$T = 2\pi\sqrt{\frac{l}{g}}$$

where g is the gravitational field strength.

If the length l doubles, the right-hand side of the equation becomes

$$2\pi\sqrt{\frac{2l}{g}}$$

that is, it is $\sqrt{2}$ (≈ 1.4) times larger than before. Therefore the period T increases by a factor of $\sqrt{2}$.

Here we say the period is proportional to the square root of the length; if the length doubles, the period increases by a factor $\sqrt{2}$; if the length quadruples the period doubles, and so on.

Example 4

The equation for the force between two bodies with electric charges Q_1 and Q_2 is given by:

$$F = \frac{Q_1 Q_2}{4\pi\varepsilon_0 r^2}$$

If the distance r doubles, the right-hand side of the equation becomes

$$\frac{Q_1 Q_2}{4\pi\varepsilon_0 (2r)^2}$$

that is, it is $(\frac{1}{2})^2 = \frac{1}{4}$ of its original value; therefore the force F reduces to $\frac{1}{4}$ of its original value.

In this case the force F is inversely proportional to the square of the distance r.

Example 5

In some situations, more than one variable is changed. For example, suppose a piece of wire has its length doubled and its cross-sectional area halved; what will be the effect on its resistance?

The relevant equation is

$$R = \frac{\rho l}{A}$$

If l is doubled and A is halved, the right-hand side becomes

$$\frac{\rho(2l)}{(\frac{1}{2}A)} \quad \text{or} \quad \frac{4\rho l}{A}$$

which is 4 times larger than before. Therefore the resistance increases by a factor of 4.

✍ Student task 1.6

A piece of wire has both its length and its diameter doubled; what will be the effect on its resistance?

(First show that if the diameter doubles the cross-sectional area quadruples, then use the same equation as in the example above the calculate the effect on the resistance.)

✤ Pitfall 1.5

Watch out for **dependent** variables in equations, that is, where changes in one variable also affect another one. In all the previous examples, the variables on the right-hand side of the equations do not depend on each other (for example, the length l does not affect g in example 3; the length l does not depend on the area A in example 4).

However, consider the equation for the escape velocity from a planet:

$$v_{esc} = \sqrt{\frac{2GM}{R}}$$

By what factor is the escape velocity v_{esc} changed on a planet made of the same material but of twice the radius?

The obvious answer is to say that since the radius R has doubled, the right-hand side of the equation reduces by a factor of $\sqrt{2}$ therefore the escape velocity v_{esc} also reduces by a factor of $\sqrt{2}$.

Wrong! (This implies it is easier to jump off a larger planet!) We have overlooked the fact that the mass M also increases.

In cases like this, we must put all the variables which depend on each other in terms of just one of them; in this case we could put the mass in terms of the radius as follows:

$$M = density \times volume$$

$$M = \rho \times \frac{4\pi R^3}{3}$$

hence the equation can be rewritten as follows:

$$v_{esc} = \sqrt{\frac{2G\rho 4\pi}{3}\frac{R^3}{R}}$$

$$v_{esc} = \sqrt{\frac{2G\rho 4\pi R^2}{3}}$$

$$v_{esc} = R\sqrt{\frac{2G\rho 4\pi}{3}}$$

Since all the quantities inside the square root are constant, v_{esc} is proportional to R, so if we double the radius we will double the escape velocity.

2.1 INTRODUCTION

One important characteristic of Physics is that it is frequently concerned with **quantifying** observations. It has been said that if something cannot be measured, it is of no interest to a physicist. Although this is undoubtedly a gross exaggeration, there is no doubt that you must be reasonably adept at handling numbers if you are to be a competent physicist. Much of this handling of numbers is little more than simple arithmetic, and much of this simple arithmetic will be done using a calculator.

2.2 USING A CALCULATOR

You must be able to use a calculator with confidence. It is assumed that you can carry out simple, single operations such as adding, multiplying, finding a square root and so on, but there a number of pitfalls for the unwary if you have to carry out a **sequence** of operations. Your calculator will have a set of rules which tell it in which order to do some calculations, and it might not be doing calculations in the same order as you think you are instructing it.

Most calculators follow the 'BODMAS' rule (Brackets, Of, Divide, Multiply, Add, Subtract). This means they will deal with any calculations inside brackets first, and so on, finishing with addition and subtraction. The following common pitfalls give some examples of how this rule operates. If your calculator does **not** follow the BODMAS rule, then you must refer to your calculator handbook to see how to do these calculations. If you are not sure which rule your calculator follows, try the calculation in Pitfall 2.1; if you obtain the answer 14, your calculator does follow the BODMAS rule, if you obtain 18 it does not.

✷ *Pitfall 2.1*

Calculate $2 + 4 \times 3$

Even though you key in the calculation in the order it is written above, your calculator will **first** multiply 4 by 3 and **then** add 2 to the result. The key presses and the resulting calculator displays are as follows:

Key press	Display shows
2	2
+	2
4	4
×	4
3	3
=	14

If you intended to add 2 to 4, and then multiply the result by 3 (to give 18) you must force the calculator to add 2 and 4 first. There are two ways of doing this, as follows:

1. Break the calculation into two stages thus:

$$2 + 4 = \text{first result}$$

$$\text{first result} \times 3 = \text{final result}$$

Key press	Display shows
2	2
+	2
4	4
=	6
×	6
3	3
=	18

2. Place brackets round $2 + 4$, so that the calculator does this part first. The calculation then looks like:

$$(2 + 4) \times 3$$

Key press	Display shows
(	(1 0
2	2
+	2
4	4
)	6
×	6
3	3
=	18

The number 1 after the first bracket on the display is not part of the calculation; brackets can be 'nested' on many calculators, that is, there can be brackets within brackets, up to some limit. The number 1 tells you this is the first set of brackets to be opened. There is, of course, only one set of brackets in this calculation.

✍ Student task 2.1

A calculator will give an answer of 28 to the calculation $6 + 5 \times 3 + 7$

How would you arrange brackets round these figures so that the answer was:

a) 110   b) 56   c) 40 ?

✳ Pitfall 2.2

Calculate $\dfrac{2 + 4 \times 3}{7}$

All of the numerator (the top line of the fraction) must be evaluated first, before dividing by 7. However, unless you instruct it otherwise, your calculator will multiply 4 by 3, and divide the answer by 7, before adding 2, thus giving an incorrect answer of 3.714.

One correct set of key presses is:

2 + 4 x 3 = ÷ 7 =

✍ Student task 2.2

What is another correct set of key presses to carry out this calculation?

✳ Pitfall 2.3

Calculate $\dfrac{2 \times 10}{5 \times 3}$

A very common mistake is to key in:

2 x 10 ÷ 5 x 3

giving an incorrect answer of 12. Your calculator evaluates 2 × 10 (= 20), divides the answer by 5 (= 4) and then multiplies this answer by 3, to give the final incorrect answer of 12. It is not clear to the calculator that the 3 is part of the denominator.

One correct set of key presses is:

2 x 10 ÷ 5 ÷ 3 =

✍ Student task 2.3

What is another correct set of key presses to carry out this calculation?

✳ Pitfall 2.4

It is important to remember that function buttons, such as x^2, $\sqrt{x}$ and sin x act on the number shown on the display at the time the keys are pressed.

For example, calculate $\sqrt{5 \times 9}$

The correct sequence of presses is as follows:

Key press	Display shows
5	5
×	5
9	9
=	45
√x	6.7082

whereas a common incorrect sequence is

5 x 9 √x =

giving an answer of 15; in this case the calculator has evaluated the square root of 9, and multiplied it by 5, rather than evaluating the square root of 45 as intended.

2.3 STANDARD FORM

Many of the numbers we meet in Physics are either very large or very small.

For example, the mass of the earth is:

5 980 000 000 000 000 000 000 000 kg

while the charge on an electron is:

0.000 000 000 000 000 000 16 C

It is clearly ludicrous to try to do calculations with numbers written like this. You cannot key them into your calculator for a start, and it would be very easy to make a mistake with the number of zeros. In order to overcome this problem, we write numbers in standard form. A number is expressed as a number between 1 and 10 multiplied by an appropriate power of 10.

For example, 347 can be written as 3.47×100, or 3.47×10^2.

3.47×10^2 is known as **standard form.**

Using standard form, the mass of the earth can be written as 5.98×10^{24} kg, and the charge on an electron as 1.6×10^{-19} C.

This is clearly a much more convenient way to write such numbers, but there are other good reasons for using standard form, outlined in the following sections. It is very important that you should be able to handle standard form easily.

2.4 CONVERTING TO STANDARD FORM

To convert 37 800 to standard form.

The number between 1 and 10 which is needed is 3.78.

37 800 is $3.78 \times 10\,000$. 10 000 is 10^4 (see Table 2.1) so 37 800 in standard form is 3.78×10^4.

An alternative approach is to say that to go from 3.78 to 37 800, the numbers must move 4 places to the left, as follows:

3.78

37.8

378.0

3 780.0

37 800.0

Therefore the power of 10 required is 4, and 37 800 in standard form is 3.78×10^4.

To convert 0.0052 to standard form.

The number between 1 and 10 which is needed is 5.2. 0.0052 is 5.2×0.001. 0.001 is 10^{-3}, so 0.0052 in standard form is 5.2×10^{-3}.

Alternatively, to go from 5.2 to 0.0052 the numbers must be moved 3 places to the right, therefore the required power is -3, and 0.0052 in standard form is 5.2×10^{-3}.

Table 2.1

$10^6 =$	1 000 000
$10^4 =$	10 000
$10^3 =$	1000
$10^1 =$	10
$10^0 =$	1
$10^{-1} =$	0.1
$10^{-3} =$	0.001
$10^{-6} =$	0.000 001

✍ *Student task 2.4*

Convert the following numbers to standard form:

a)   3470

b)   68 000 000

c)   27

d)   0.594

e)   0.000 92

f)   264.2

2.5 STANDARD FORM AND CALCULATORS

Note: Not all calculators are operated in the same way; you may need to refer to the instructions for your own calculator and modify what follows accordingly.

To key in a number to your calculator in standard form, you will need to use the **EXP** button. EXP standards for '**exponent**' and means '**multiplied by 10 to the power of**'.

For example

to key 3.78×10^5 into your calculator:

Key press	Display shows
3.78	3.78
EXP	3.78 00
5	3.78 05

This means $\mathbf{3.78 \times 10^5}$

(Some calculators will change this display to 378000 when you press the next button to carry on with your calculation. Other calculators can be programmed to keep all numbers in standard form.)

To key 5.2×10^{-3} into your calculator, the correct set of key presses is:

$$5.2 \quad \text{EXP} \quad \pm \quad 3$$

Your calculator display should now show something similar to

$$5.2 \ -03$$

This means 5.2×10^{-3}

✎ **Student task 2.5**

Key the following numbers into your calculator:

a) 5.89×10^{24}

b) 6.36×10^6

c) 1.60×10^{-19}

d) 6.63×10^{-34}

✱ *Pitfall 2.5*

Remember that a number like 10^8 by itself in a calculation really means 1×10^8, and must be keyed into your calculator as 1 EXP 8, not 10 EXP 8.

Example:

10^8 *C of electric charge flow round an electric circuit in a year. What is the average current flowing?*

$$Current \ = \ \frac{charge}{time}$$

$$Current \ = \ \frac{10^8 \ C}{365 \times 24 \times 60 \times 60 \ s}$$

Key into your calculator:

$$1 \text{ EXP } 8 \div 365 \div 24 \div 60 \div 60 =$$

giving an answer of 3.2 A

NOT

$$10 \text{ EXP } 8 \div 365 \div 24 \div 60 \div 60 =$$

giving 32 A.

✱ *Pitfall 2.6*

It is a common mistake to misinterpret a calculator display at the end of a calculation.

Example:

A stress of 1.2×10^8 N m^{-2} produces a strain of 1.5×10^{-3} in a length of wire. What is the Young modulus for this wire?

$$Young \ modulus \ = \ \frac{stress}{strain}$$

$$Young \ modulus \ = \ \frac{1.2 \times 10^8 \ N \ m^{-2}}{1.5 \times 10^{-3}}$$

Key into your calculator

$$1.2 \text{ EXP } 8 \div 1.5 \text{ EXP } \pm 3 =$$

and your display should show

$$8. \ 10$$

This means 8×10^{10}, *not* 8^{10}, so the Young modulus is 8×10^{10} N m^{-2}.

Think of the difference between $4^2 (= 16)$ and $4 \times 10^2 (= 400)$.

2.6 SIGNIFICANT FIGURES

The significant figures in a number are all the digits except any zeros before the first non-zero digit.

For example: 42, 4.2, 0.0042 and 4.2×10^6 all have 2 significant figures

                   402 and 4.02   have 3 significant figures

The number of significant figures has an important meaning to a scientist. It gives you some idea of the **precision** or **reliability** of that number.

For example, you might measure the length of a piece of wood quite roughly as being 5 cm; this means you are certain of its length to the nearest centimetre - its actual length could be anywhere between 4½ and 5½ cm.

If you measure the length more carefully, you might be able to give the measurement to 2 significant figures, 5.1 cm, for example. This means you are now more certain of the length than you were before; you are probably certain to the nearest 0.1 cm. (Section 2.9, on uncertainties, goes into more detail).

3 significant figures, such as 5.13 cm, indicates an even greater precision.

Notice that the numbers 8, 8.0 and 8.00 do not all mean the same; 8.00 (3 significant figures) implies a much greater precision than 8 (1 significant figure).

A problem can arise over interpreting some numbers if we do not use standard form. Suppose we measure the length of a road as 3200 m. It is not clear whether you have measured to the nearest 100 m, and are giving a measurement to 2 significant figures, or to the nearest metre and all 4 figures are significant. If you write the measurement using standard form, 3.2×10^3 m (2 significant figures) or 3.200×10^3 m (4 significant figures), the precision of the measurement is immediately clear.

2.7 SIGNIFICANT FIGURES AND CALCULATIONS

The answer to a calculation cannot be any more precise than the least reliable piece of data used for that calculation. It is therefore important that your answer to any calculation is rounded to the correct number of significant figures; as a good rule of thumb, this should be the same number of significant figures as your least reliable piece of data. For the data which occurs in typical A-level questions, 2 significant figures is usually right; you may lose marks in an examination if you do not round your answer to a sensible number of significant figures.

Example

A copper block has a mass of 246.3 g. It measures 2.2 cm by 3.0 cm by 4.5 cm. What is the density of the copper?

$$density = \frac{mass}{volume}$$

$$density = \frac{246.3 \text{ g}}{2.2 \text{ cm} \times 3.0 \text{ cm} \times 4.5 \text{ cm}}$$

$$density = 8.292\,929\,3 \text{ g cm}^{-3}$$

according to a calculator.

But this implies a precision far greater than any of the measurements that were made. The lengths were measured to 2 significant figures, so the answer must be rounded to 2 significant figures, giving a density of 8.3 g cm^{-3}.

Notice that the mass of the block was measured with a greater precision than was necessary. It is usually a waste of time making one measurement much more precise than any of the others.

✍ *Student task 2.6*

Try repeating the calculation with a mass of 246 g, or even 245 g.

2.8 UNITS AND STANDARD FORM

Quantities are often quoted in standard multiples or divisions of the basic units. The standard prefixes, together with the factor by which they multiply the basic unit, are listed in table 2.2 below.

Table 2.2

Name	Abbreviation	Multiplying factor
pico	p	10^{-12}
nano	n	10^{-9}
micro	μ	10^{-6}
milli	m	10^{-3}
kilo	k	10^{3}
mega	M	10^{6}
giga	G	10^{9}
tera	T	10^{12}

For example

1 millimetre = 1 thousandth of a metre

$$= 1 \times 10^{-3} \text{ m}$$

$$4.6 \text{ kW} = 4.6 \times 10^3 \text{ W}$$

✍ **Student task 2.7**

Write the following in standard form.

a)   7.21 μV

b)   42 GW

c)   0.39 nF

d)   592 MJ

e)   0.019 pA

Quantities often have to be written in terms of the basic unit before a calculation can be performed. This can easily be done by inserting the appropriate power of 10 in place of the prefix, and is best done by writing out a table of the relevant information before you start, as in the example in the next column. (It is a good habit to write out a table of information for anything but the simplest calculation whether or not you have to do any unit conversions.)

Example

An electric power cable has a diameter of 6.0 mm and is made of a material of resistivity 27 nΩ m. What is the resistance of a 1.0 km length of the cable?

Table of information:

Diameter = 6.0 mm	$= 6.0 \times 10^{-3}$ m
Hence radius	$= 3.0 \times 10^{-3}$ m
Length = 1.0 km	$= 1.0 \times 10^{3}$ m
Resistivity = 27 nΩ m	$= 27 \times 10^{-9}$ Ω m
Resistivity	$= 2.7 \times 10^{-8}$ Ω m

Calculation:

$$\text{Cross section area } (CSA) = \pi r^2$$

$$CSA = \pi \times 3.0 \times 10^{-3} \times 3.0 \times 10^{-3} \text{ m}^2$$

$$CSA = 2.827 \times 10^{-5} \text{ m}^2$$

$$\text{Using } R = \frac{\rho l}{A}$$

$$\left(Resistance = \frac{resistivity \times length}{area} \right)$$

$$R = \frac{2.7 \times 10^{-8} \text{ Ω m} \times 1.0 \times 10^{3} \text{ m}}{2.827 \times 10^{-5} \text{ m}^2}$$

$$R = 0.96 \text{ Ω}$$

The resistance is 0.96 Ω.

✱ *Pitfall 2.7*

Mistakes are often made in converting areas and volumes into the basic units, such as square millimetres into square metres.

Note

10^4 square centimetres = 1 square metre.

10^6 square millimetres = 1 square metre

10^6 cubic centimetres = 1 cubic metre

10^9 cubic millimetres = 1 cubic metre

✍ **Student task 2.8**

Calculate the resistance between the faces of a wafer of pure silicon of thickness 5 mm and cross section area 8.0 cm². The resistivity of silicon is 60 Ω m.

(Unlike the question above, you have been told the area, not the diameter.)

2.9 UNCERTAINTIES

We can never be absolutely sure of any physical measurement that we might make. Even if there is no error in the manufacture or calibration of the measuring instrument, then there is always a limit to how certain we can be over reading the scale. With an analogue meter there is a limit to how well we can estimate fractions of a division on a scale; with a digital meter we can be no more certain than ±1 on the last figure on the display.

You read in section 2.6 that the number of significant figures in a reading indicates how certain we are of that reading, and that there must be an uncertainty over the result of a calculation; this uncertainty can be estimated.

We can express the uncertainty of a reading either as an absolute value, or as a percentage of that reading.

For example

(4.3 ± 0.1) A (absolute value - the current lies between 4.2 A and 4.4 A).

$(7.6 \pm 0.2) \times 10^4$ m (absolute value. Note the use of brackets in this and the above example.)

5.6 kΩ ± 10% (percentage - the resistance lies between about 5.0 kΩ and 6.2 kΩ).

If several numbers are combined together in an equation, then their uncertainties are combined together according to the following rules:

Rule 1

If two numbers are added or subtracted, then the **absolute** values of the uncertainties are **added** (the uncertainties must obviously be in the same units).

For example:

(4.2 ± 0.1) m + (1.6 ± 0.2) m = (5.8 ± 0.3) m

Rule 2

If two numbers are multiplied or divided, then the **percentage** uncertainties of each number are **added**.

For example

The p.d. across a lamp is 8.2 V ± 10% and the current through the lamp is 2.2 A ± 15%. What is the power dissipated in the lamp?

$Power = p.d. \times current$

$Power = 8.2$ V $\times 2.2$ A

$Power = 18$ W

Uncertainty = 10% + 15%

hence *power* = 18 W ± 25% or (18 ± 5) W

Rule 3

If a number is squared, its percentage uncertainty doubles; if it is cubed, the percentage uncertainty triples, and so on. The percentage uncertainty of the square root of a number is half that of the original number.

For example

The radius of a brass sphere is 4.3 cm ± 5%; what is its volume?

$$Volume = \frac{4}{3} \pi r^3$$

$$Volume = \frac{4}{3} \pi \times (4.3)^3$$

$$Volume = 330 \text{ cm}^3$$

$$Uncertainty = 3 \times 5\% = 15\%$$

$$\therefore volume = 330 \text{ cm}^3 \pm 15\%$$

$$\text{or } (330 \pm 50) \text{ cm}^3$$

✍ *Student task 2.9*

What is the speed of sound in aluminium?

Data for aluminium:

Young modulus = $(7.2 \pm 0.2) \times 10^{10}$ N m⁻²

density = $(2.6 \pm 0.3) \times 10^3$ kg m⁻³.

$$speed \ of \ sound = \sqrt{\frac{Young \ modulus}{density}}$$

2.10 ROUGH CALCULATIONS

It is very easy to key the wrong number into a calculator, so it is often sensible to carry out a rough calculation with your figures, if only to check that you have the correct order of magnitude (that is, power of 10).

To do this, you need to know the rules about multiplying and dividing powers of 10; these were shown in Table 1.3 (Handling indices) and a few more examples are given in Table 2.3 below.

Example

A straight conductor of length 50 mm carries an electric current of 1.2 A. When it is placed perpendicular to a magnetic field it experiences a force of 4.5 mN. What was the strength of the magnetic field?

Table of information:

Conductor length (l) = 50 mm   = 5×10^{-2} m

Electric current (I)   = 1.2 A

Force (F) = 4.5 mN   = 4.5×10^{-3} N

Rough calculation

Using $B = \dfrac{F}{Il}$

$$B = \frac{4.5 \times 10^{-3}\ \text{N}}{1.2\ \text{A} \times 5 \times 10^{-2}\ \text{m}}$$

Deal with the numbers first, forgetting about the powers of 10:

$$\frac{4.5}{1.2 \times 5} \approx \frac{1}{1.2} \approx 0.8$$

Now the powers of 10:

$$\frac{10^{-3}}{10^{-2}} = 10^{-3-(-2)} = 10^{-1}$$

Thus the field strength is roughly

$$0.8 \times 10^{-1} \text{ or } 8 \times 10^{-2} \text{ T}$$

(A calculator gives 7.5×10^{-2} T.)

Table 2.3 Handling powers of 10

$$10^2 \times 10^4 = 10^{2+4} = 10^6$$

$$\frac{10^2}{10^6} = 10^{2-6} = 10^{-4}$$

$$(10^3)^2 = 10^{3 \times 2} = 10^6$$

$$\sqrt{10^8} = 10^{8 \div 2} = 10^4$$

$$\sqrt{10^5} = \sqrt{10^1} \times \sqrt{10^4} \approx 3 \times 10^2$$

Notice how to deal with the square root of an odd numbered power of 10 in the last example, and that $\sqrt{10} \approx 3$ (more accurately, $\sqrt{10} \approx \pi$).

✍ Student task 2.10

A weather satellite orbits at a distance of 1.0×10^6 m above the surface of the earth. What is the approximate speed of the satellite?

(The radius of the earth is 6.37×10^6 m and GM for the earth is 4.0×10^{14} N m^2 kg^{-1}.

To start you off, use

centripetal force = gravitational force

$$\frac{mv^2}{r} = \frac{GMm}{r^2}$$

$$\therefore v = \sqrt{\frac{GM}{r}}$$

3 *Angles*

3.1 INTRODUCTION

An understanding of angles is particularly vital in Physics when handling **vector** quantities. A vector quantity is one with **direction** as well as magnitude. Displacement, force and field are all examples of vector quantities. A quantity with magnitude only, such as temperature, is called a **scalar** quantity.

An understanding of angles is also necessary when studying circular motion and the behaviour of waves.

3.2 FACTS ABOUT TRIANGLES

a) For any triangle, the sum of the three internal angles is 180°.

In Figure 3.1, $x + y + z = 180°$.

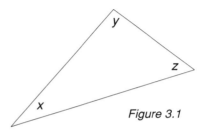

Figure 3.1

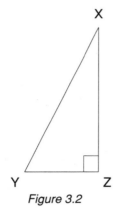

Figure 3.2

b) Figure 3.2 shows a right-angled triangle. The side XY opposite the right angle is called the **hypotenuse**.

Pythagoras' theorem states 'the square of the hypotenuse is equal to the sum of the squares of the other two sides' - or, more simply, referring to figure 3.2:

$$(XY)^2 = (XZ)^2 + (YZ)^2$$

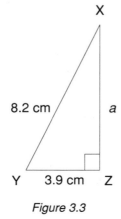

Figure 3.3

Example

In Figure 3.3, what is the length of side a?

Using Pythagoras' theorem:

$$8.2^2 = 3.9^2 + a^2$$

$$\therefore a^2 = 8.2^2 - 3.9^2$$

$$\therefore a = \sqrt{8.2^2 - 3.9^2}$$

Calculator key presses:

$$8.2 \ x^2 \ - \ 3.9 \ x^2 \ = \ \sqrt{x}$$

giving $a = 7.2$ cm.

c) The area of a triangle is calculated from:

$$area = \frac{1}{2} \times base \times height$$

Example 1

In Figure 3.4:

$$area = \frac{1}{2} \times 7 \text{ cm} \times 5 \text{ cm}$$
$$area = 17.5 \text{ cm}^2$$

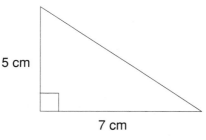

Figure 3.4

Example 2

In Figure 3.5:

$$area = \frac{1}{2} \times 12 \text{ cm} \times 5 \text{ cm}$$
$$area = 30 \text{ cm}^2$$

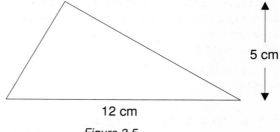

Figure 3.5

✳ Pitfall 3.1

Notice that, when calculating the area of a triangle, the height must be the **vertical** height.

✍ Student task 3.1

For each of the three triangles shown in Figure 3.6, calculate:

i)   the angle x;

ii)   the length y;

iii)   the area of the triangle.

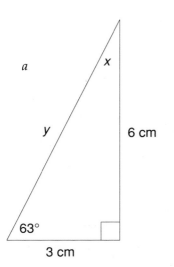

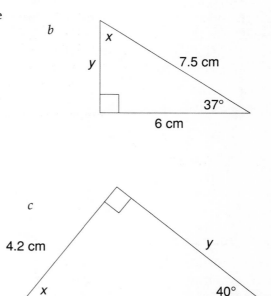

Figure 3.6

3.3 SINES, COSINES AND TANGENTS

The right-angled triangle is used to define three important functions of angles - sine, cosine and tangent.

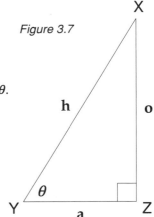

Figure 3.7

Figure 3.7 shows a right-angled triangle.

Side XY, labelled **h**, is the **h**ypotenuse.

Side YZ, labelled **a**, is the side **a**djacent to angle θ.

Side XZ, labelled **o**, is the side **o**pposite angle θ.

$\sin\theta = \frac{o}{h}$ (sin is the abbreviation for sine)

$\cos\theta = \frac{a}{h}$ (cos is the abbreviation for cosine)

$\tan\theta = \frac{o}{a}$ (tan is the abbreviation for tanget)

Some people find a simple sentence useful to help remember these relationships. One example is:

Silly Old Harry Caught A Herring Trawling Off Afghanistan.

The first letter of each word describes the three relationships. For example:

$$\textbf{CAH} \quad \text{Cosine} = \frac{\text{Adjacent}}{\text{Hypotenuse}}$$

Using your calculator

To use a calculator to find the sine, cosine or tangent of an angle, simply key in the angle and press the sin, cos or tan key as appropriate.

For example, to find the sine of 27°, key in 27 and press sin, to give **0.454** (to 3 significant figures) on the display.

✍ *Student task 3.2*

Use a calculator to find:

a)   cos 81°

b)   tan 37°

c)   sin 66°

If you know the value of the sine, cosine or tangent of an angle, to find the corresponding angle use the sin⁻¹, cos⁻¹ or tan⁻¹ key as appropriate.

(These keys might be marked something like 'arcsin', 'asn' or 'invsin' on your calculator.)

For example, to find the angle whose cosine is 0.62, key in 0.62 and press cos⁻¹, giving an angle of 51.7°.

✍ *Student task 3.3*

Use a calculator to find the following values of θ:

a) $\sin\theta = 0.32$

b) $\cos\theta = 0.27$

c) $\tan\theta = 1.61$

Some useful values of sines, cosines and tangents are shown in Table 3.1 below.

Table 3.1

angle	sine	cosine	tangent
0	0	1	0
30	0.5	$\frac{\sqrt{3}}{2} = 0.87$	$\frac{1}{\sqrt{3}} = 0.58$
45	$\frac{1}{\sqrt{2}} = 0.71$	$\frac{1}{\sqrt{2}} = 0.71$	1
60	$\frac{\sqrt{3}}{2} = 0.87$	0.5	$\sqrt{3} = 1.73$
90	1	0	∞

Two useful relationships

Two useful relationships between the sine, cosine and tangent of an angle are:

i) $\quad \sin^2\theta + \cos^2\theta = 1$

ii) $\quad \dfrac{\sin\theta}{\cos\theta} = \tan\theta$

✳ Pitfall 3.2

Notice the notation used above - $\sin^2\theta$, not $\sin\theta^2$. $\sin^2\theta$ means 'find the sine of the angle and then square the result'.

For example, to find $\sin^2 40°$:

$$\sin 40° = 0.643$$
$$(0.643)^2 = 0.413$$
$$\therefore \sin^2 40° = 0.413$$

$\sin\theta^2$ means 'square the angle, then find the sine of the result' - but a squared angle has no meaning in A-level Physics!

Example

Find the lengths of XY and XZ in the triangle in Figure 3.8.

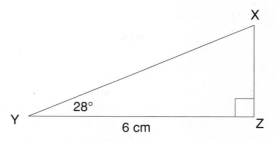

To find the length of XZ:

XZ is **opposite** the angle of 28°, so we will use the **tan** relationship:

$$\frac{XZ}{6 \text{ cm}} = \tan 28°$$

$$\therefore \ XZ = 6 \text{ cm} \times \tan 28°$$

Calculator key presses:

Key press	Display shows
6	6
×	6
28	28
TAN	0.5317094
=	3.1902566

$$\therefore XZ = 3.2 \text{ cm.}$$

To find the length of XY

$$\frac{6 \text{ cm}}{XY} = \cos 28°$$
$$6 \text{ cm} = XY \times \cos 28°$$
$$\therefore \ XY = \frac{6 \text{ cm}}{\cos 28°}$$
$$XY = 6.80 \text{ cm}$$

✎ Student task 3.4

An alternative way of calculating the value of side XY is to use Pythagoras' theorem, since the lengths of XZ and YZ are now known.

Use Pythagoras' theorem to confirm that XY is of length 6.80 cm.

✍ *Student task 3.5*

For each of the following triangles, find the values of the angles and lengths which are marked with a letter.

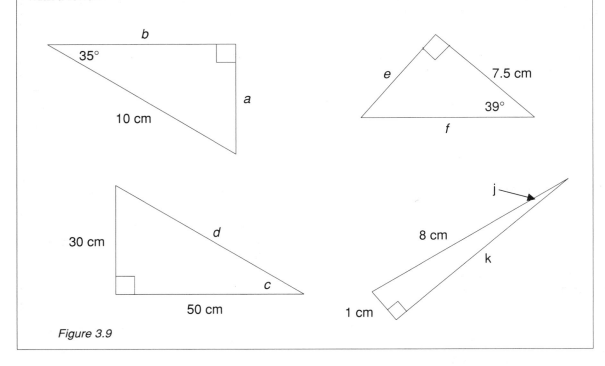

Figure 3.9

3.4 THE RESULTANT OF TWO VECTORS

Here is a simple-sounding problem.

A girl walks 4 m in a straight line. She then walks a further 10 m in a straight line. How far from her starting point is she when she finishes? (In other words, what is her total **displacement**?)

We cannot work out an answer. She has walked a total **distance** of 14 m, but she may have changed direction after the first 4 m. Her total **displacement** could be anything between 6 m and 14 m in an unknown direction from the start. Distance is a **scalar** quantity but displacement is a **vector** - we need to know the directions in which she walks, and we do not have that information.

Here is a similar question with all the required information.

A girl walks 4 m due north in a straight line. She then walks a further 10 m due east in a straight line. What is her resultant displacement? (That is, how far is she from the start, and in what direction?)

A diagram of her journey is shown in Figure 3.10.

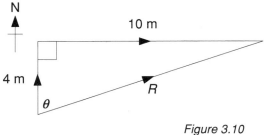

Figure 3.10

22

Notice the terminology that is used:

R is the **resultant** displacement.

10 m east and 4 m north are the **components** (or 'parts') of that displacement.

Referring to Figure 3.10, R can be calculated using Pythagoras' theorem:

$$R^2 = 10^2 + 4^2$$

$$\therefore R = \sqrt{116}$$

$$R = 10.8 \text{ m}$$

θ is calculated using the tan relationship:

$$\tan \theta = \frac{10}{4}$$

$$\therefore \theta = 68.2°$$

Therefore the resultant displacement is 10.8 m in a direction 68.2° east of north.

The resultant vector is not necessarily along the hypotenuse of a right-angled triangle, as the following example shows.

Example

A person can row a boat at 3 m/s relative to the water. He wishes to row to a point directly across a river 20 m wide which is flowing at 2 m/s. In which direction must he point the boat, and what is the magnitude of the resultant velocity?

The vector diagram for this situation is shown in Figure 3.11.

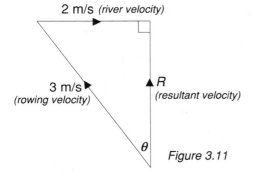

2 m/s *(river velocity)*

3 m/s
(rowing velocity)

R
(resultant velocity)

θ

Figure 3.11

✍ *Student task 3.6*

Making use of figure 3.11, show that:

a) the magnitude of the resultant velocity R is 2.2 m/s.

b) θ is 42°.

c) it takes about 9 s to row across the river.

✍ *Student task 3.7*

For each of the situations below, find the magnitude and direction of the resultant vector.

a)
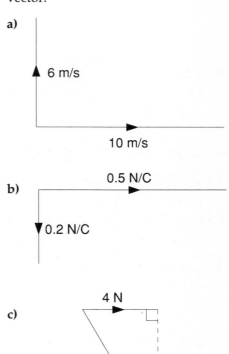

6 m/s

10 m/s

b)

0.5 N/C

0.2 N/C

c)
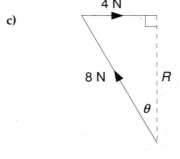

4 N

8 N R

θ

Figure 3.12

3.5 THE COMPONENTS OF A VECTOR

Finding the components (or 'parts') of a single vector is the opposite process to that described in the last section.

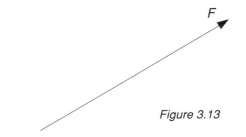

Figure 3.13

Suppose a force F acts in some direction as shown in Figure 3.13.

The force F has a **component** in any direction you choose, that is, it partly acts in that direction (although the component at right angles to the direction of the force is zero). Often a Physics problem requires us to look at two components perpendicular to each other, typically in the horizontal direction and the vertical direction, as shown in Figure 3.14.

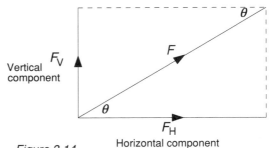

Figure 3.14

Using the usual trigonometry relations:

$$\frac{F_H}{F} = \cos\theta \quad \therefore F_H = F\cos\theta$$

$$\frac{F_V}{F} = \sin\theta \quad \therefore F_V = F\sin\theta$$

$$\left(\text{Note also that } \frac{F_V}{F_H} = \tan\theta\right)$$

Example

An electric field of 5 N/C acts at an angle of 30° to the horizontal. What are the vertical and horizontal components of this field?

Figure 3.15 shows the vector diagram for this problem.

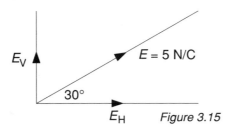

Figure 3.15

$$E_H = 5\cos30° = 5\frac{\sqrt{3}}{2} = 4.3\,\text{N/C}$$

$$E_V = 5\sin30° = 5\times0.5 = 2.5\,\text{N/C}$$

✷ Pitfall 3.3

Look carefully at which angle you know when calculating the two components. In Figure 3.14, θ is the angle between the vector and the horizontal. If you know the angle between the vector and the vertical is φ, for example, then $F_H = F\sin\varphi$.

✍ Student task 3.8

A person cycles at 6 m/s in a direction 130° east of north. What are the components of the cyclist's velocity in an easterly and a southerly direction?

The vector diagram for this problem is shown in Figure 3.16.

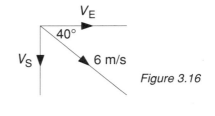

Figure 3.16

A picture of weight 4 N is hung by a piece of string as shown in Figure 3.17. What is the tension in the string?

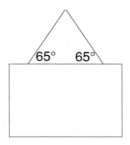

Figure 3.17

Look at Figure 3.18. This shows the forces acting on the picture, with the tension T resolved into vertical and horizontal components T_V and T_H.

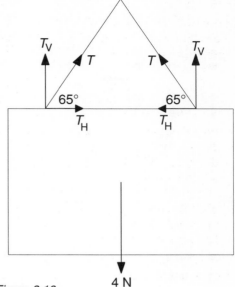

Figure 3.18

✎ Student task 3.9

Using this information, calculate the tension T in the string.

3.6 RADIANS

As well as being measured in degrees, angles can be measured in units called **radians**.

Look at Figure 3.19. This shows a circle with a segment AOB. The angle θ depends on the arc length AB ($= s$) as well as the radius r. If the ratio $s/r = 1$ (that is, the arc length $s = $ the radius r) then the angle $\theta = 1$ **radian** (1 rad).

In general, θ rad $= \dfrac{\text{arc length}}{\text{radius}} = \dfrac{s}{r}$

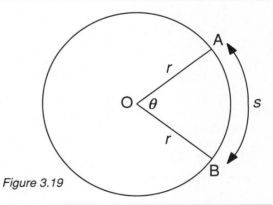

Figure 3.19

An angle of 360° corresponds to an arc length equal to the circumference of a circle, which is equal to $2\pi r$. In this case,

$$\theta = \frac{\text{arc length}}{\text{radius}} = \frac{2\pi r}{r} = 2\pi \text{ rad}$$

Thus 360° = 2π rad, or

$$1 \text{ rad} = \frac{360°}{2\pi} \approx 57°$$

✎ Student task 3.10

a) How many radians are there in:
   i) 20°; ii) 75°; iii) 90°?

b) How many degrees are there in:
   i) 0.4 rad; ii) 0.75 rad; iii) 1.6 rad?

c) In a circle like the one in Figure 3.19, if the radius is 10 m and the arc length is 2.2 m, what is the angle θ in radians?

d) A segment of a circle has an angle of 1.2 rad. If the radius of the circle is 6 cm, what is the arc length?

3.7 THE SMALL ANGLE APPROXIMATION

Figure 3.20 shows a segment OAB of a circle, within which is marked a right-angled triangle OAC. The arc length from A to B ($=s$) is greater than the distance AC ($=x$).

$$s = r\theta$$
$$x = r\sin\theta$$

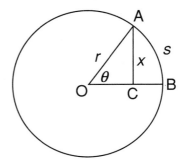

Figure 3.20

If the angle θ is much smaller so that the situation is as illustrated in Figure 3.21, the arc length AB is virtually the same as the length of AC, so, for small angles (< 0.2 rad)

$$r\sin\theta \approx r\theta$$
$$\therefore \ \sin\theta \approx \theta$$

Similarly, the length of OC is almost equal to the length of OA ($= r$).

$$\therefore \ \tan\theta \ \left(= \frac{AC}{OC} \approx \frac{AC}{r}\right) \approx \sin\theta \ \left(= \frac{AC}{OA} = \frac{AC}{r}\right)$$

> In general, for small angles:
>
> $$\sin\theta \approx \tan\theta \approx \theta$$
>
> (θ measured in radians)

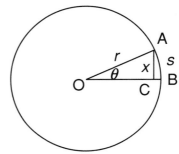

Figure 3.21

❊ *Pitfall 3.4*

It does not matter in which units you measure an angle (degrees or radians), the sine, cosine and tangent of that angle do not change in value.

For example, in Figure 3.22, the angle θ is equal to 30° or 0.52 rad. Sin θ is 0.5 (from the dimensions of the triangle) regardless of the units for θ.

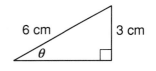

Figure 3.22

Example

A radio-telescope with a dish diameter of 25 m is used for detecting radiation of wavelength 21 cm coming from clouds of hydrogen in our galaxy. What is the smallest separation of two clouds of hydrogen which are a distance of 2×10^{20} m from the earth such that the radio-telescope can still distinguish them?

From the Rayleigh criterion for resolution, two objects will just be resolved when viewed through a circular aperture if

$$\sin\theta \geqslant \frac{1.22\lambda}{b}$$

where θ is the angle subtended by the two objects at the telescope, λ is the wavelength of the radiation and b is the diameter of the telescope dish.

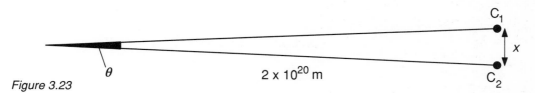

Figure 3.23

If the distance between the two clouds of hydrogen is x, as shown in Figure 3.23, then θ, measured in radians, is given by

$$\theta = \frac{x}{2 \times 10^{20}}$$

Since θ is very small, $\theta = \sin\theta$; hence, for the two clouds to be just resolved:

$$\theta = \frac{x}{2 \times 10^{20}\,\text{m}} = \frac{1.22\lambda}{b} = \frac{1.22 \times 0.21\,\text{m}}{25\,\text{m}}$$

$$\therefore x = \frac{1.22 \times 0.21\,\text{m} \times 2 \times 10^{20}\,\text{m}}{25\,\text{m}}$$

$$x = 2.0 \times 10^{18}\,\text{m}$$

The distance between the two clouds must be no less than 2.0×10^{18} m.

✍ Student task 3.11

When the planet Venus appears as the Morning Star it is about 1.5×10^8 km from the Earth. It looks perceptibly different from a true star, perhaps because the unaided eye sees it as a disc rather than a point of light. The diameter of Venus is about 12 000 km.

Using suitable estimates of the average wavelength of light and the diameter of the pupils of your eye at low light intensities, decide whether this suggestion is plausible, or does the difference in appearance between this planet and a star require some other explanation?

27

4 *Graphs*

4.1 INTRODUCTION

Fundamental to Physics is the establishment of relationships (or links) between quantities. Not only do graphs provide an instant visual indication of how one quantity changes as another is varied, but they also enable quantitative relationships to be established. This chapter is concerned with both the correct plotting of graphs and the making of a variety of deductions from graphs.

4.2 COMMON RELATIONSHIPS

In all the examples in this section, the mathematical relationship is written at the start of each section. **k** in these equations is called the 'proportionality constant'.

a) *y* directly proportional to *x*

$$y \propto x \quad \text{or} \quad y = kx$$

As *x* doubles, *y* doubles; as *x* trebles, *y* trebles.

A graph which shows direct proportionality is a *straight line through the origin*, as shown in Figure 4.1. In this case the constant of proportionality **k** is also the gradient of the graph. This is explained in more detail in Section 4.4.

Notice that the graph **must** pass through the origin. This is a particularly useful graph since its shape can be tested easily with a straight edge such as a ruler. We often manipulate data to give a straight line graph.

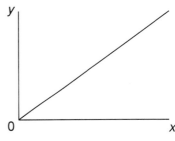

Figure 4.1

Examples of relationships which show direct proportionality include:

a) extension is proportional to force for a material which obeys Hooke's law.

b) current is proportional to potential difference for a resistor which obeys Ohm's law.

c) acceleration is proportional to force for a moving body.

❊ *Pitfall 4.1*

A straight line which does **not** pass through the origin, as in Figure 4.2, shows a 'linear' relationship between *x* and *y*, but does not show direct proportionality. Such a line has an equation of the form $y = mx + c$, where m is the gradient of the line and c is the intercept on the *y*-axis.

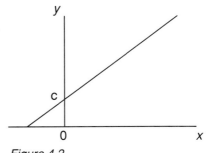

Figure 4.2

---

b) *y* inversely proportional to *x*

$$y \propto \frac{1}{x} \quad \text{or} \quad y = \frac{k}{x}$$

As *x* doubles, *y* halves; as *x* trebles, *y* becomes one third of its original value.

A graph which shows inverse proportionality is shown in Figure 4.3. Note that the line does not ever touch the *x* or the *y*-axis; it is *asymptotic* to each axis. The mathematical name for this shape is a *hyperbola*.

A physical example of this relationship is Boyle's law for a gas - the volume of a gas is inversely proportional to the pressure.

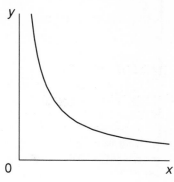

Figure 4.3

c) *y* proportional to *x* squared

$$y \propto x^2 \quad \text{or} \quad y = kx^2$$

As *x* doubles, *y* quadruples; as *x* trebles, *y* becomes nine times greater.

Figure 4.4 is a graph which shows this relationship. The graph is symmetrical about the *y*-axis, but in many situations only the positive *x* values have any physical meaning. The mathematical name for this shape is a *parabola*.

A graph of displacement against time for a body moving with constant acceleration is a parabola ($s = \frac{1}{2}at^2$).

A graph of *y* against *x* for $y^2 \propto x$ (or $y \propto \sqrt{x}$) is also parabolic, but symmetrical about the *x*-axis.

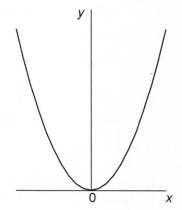

Figure 4.4

d) *y* inversely proportional to *x* squared

$$y \propto \frac{1}{x^2} \quad \text{or} \quad y = \frac{k}{x^2}$$

As *x* doubles, *y* becomes one quarter of its original value; as *x* trebles, *y* becomes one ninth of its original value.

A graph showing this 'inverse square' relationship is shown in Figure 4.5. Without a carefully study of the scales on the axes, it is not possible to tell whether a graph is inverse (as in Figure 4.3), inverse square or some other inverse relation. Sections 4.7 and 5.8 discuss techniques to decide between the different possibilities.

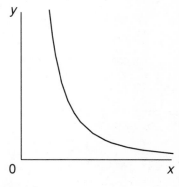

Figure 4.5

Examples of inverse square relationships in Physics include:

   a) The variation of force with distance for both electric and gravitational fields.

   b) The variation of intensity of electromagnetic radiation with distance.

29

e) y proportional to sine x or cosine x

$$y \propto \sin x \quad \text{or} \quad y = A\sin kx$$

$$y \propto \cos x \quad \text{or} \quad y = A\cos kx$$

A is a constant and is equal to the maximum value of y, that is, the value of y at the 'peak' of the graph.

Figures 4.6 and 4.7 show the sine and cosine relationship. The two graphs are essentially the same shape, but the sine graph starts at the origin, with y equal to zero, while the cosine graph starts at the maximum value for y. We say that there is a *phase difference* of 90° or $\pi/2$ radian between the two graphs.

The displacement-time and velocity-time graphs of bodies executing simple harmonic motion are of this form.

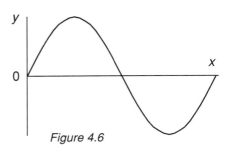

Figure 4.6

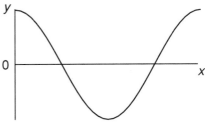

Figure 4.7

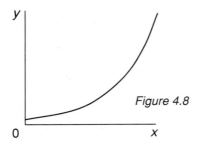

Figure 4.8

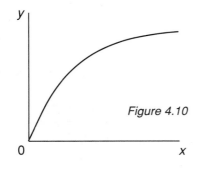

Figure 4.9

f) Exponential or logarithmic graphs

$$y \propto a^x \qquad \text{or} \qquad y = ka^{\lambda x}$$

$$y \propto a^{-x} \qquad \text{or} \qquad y = ka^{-\lambda x}$$

$$y \propto (1 - a^{-x}) \qquad \text{or} \qquad y = k(1 - a^{-\lambda x})$$

k, **a** and λ in these equations are all constants. Figures 4.8, 4,9 and 4.10 show examples of these graphs.

Figure 4.8 shows an exponential increase ($y \propto a^x$). Notice that, unlike the parabolic graph in figure 4.4 with which it could be confused, this graph does not pass through the origin.

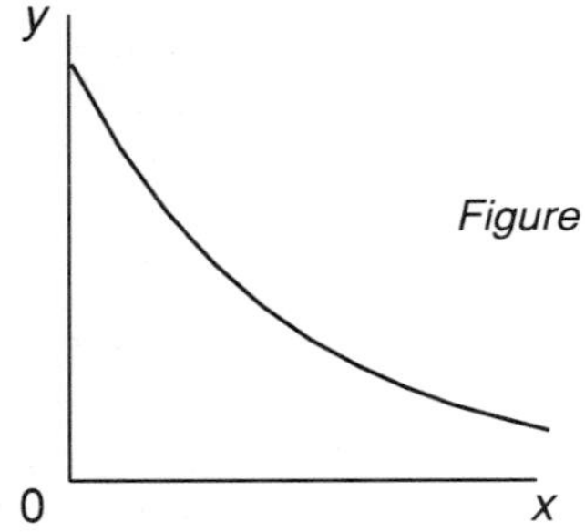

Figure 4.9 is the exponential decrease ($y \propto a^{-x}$). Notice that, unlike the inverse relationship shown in figure 4.3, this graph starts from a finite value of y; in other words, the curve touches the y-axis.

Radioactive decay and the discharge of a capacitor both show an exponential decrease relationship.

The final graph (Figure 4.10) shows an exponential relationship that builds up to a final value, such as might be found with the build up of charge on a capacitor.

Chapter 5 is devoted to a detailed look at logarithmic functions.

Figure 4.10

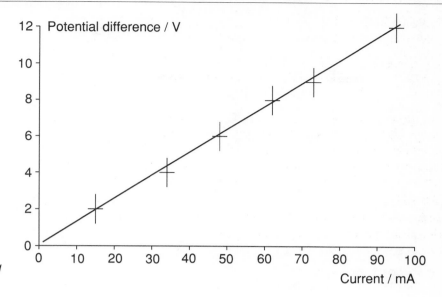

Figure 4.11

Figure 4.11 shows a correctly drawn graph of potential difference across a resistor against current through the resistor.

Notice the following points:

a) Each axis has been labelled with both the quantity and the correct unit in the form 'quantity / unit'. An alternative label for the x-axis would be 'Current / 10^{-3} A'. At first sight this form of labelling might seem odd; the reasoning behind it is as follows.

The current scale should read 10 mA, 20 mA, 30 mA, etc. The numbers that actually appear along the axis are the real values divided by 'mA'. For example,

$$\frac{10\,\text{mA}}{\text{mA}} = 10$$

Hence the label tells you what has been done to the correct current values to obtain the values shown on the axis.

b) The points have been plotted with a '+' sign, the length of each bar indicating the range over which the likely value lies, having taken into account any measuring uncertainties (see Section 2.9). This graph shows that the current was measured to ±2 mA and the potential difference to ±0.8 V.

c) As far as can be judged, the points lie on a straight line (which is what is to be expected if the conductor obeys Ohm's Law, with the current being proportional to the potential difference). Therefore the best fit straight line has been drawn which goes through the error bars of all the points.

d) There is bound to be some uncertainty over exactly where to draw the straight line, so there is some uncertainty over the value of the gradient of the graph (which is equal to the resistance). The next section deals with this in more detail.

✍ Student task 4.1

Using the data in the table below, plot a correctly labelled graph of pressure against volume, using 'error bars' of the appropriate length. Draw the best smooth curve through the points on the graph.

Pressure / 10^5 Pa (± 0.1×10^5 Pa)	1.0	1.3	1.5	1.8	2.0	2.2	2.5
Volume / cm^3 (± 3 cm^3)	50	37	32	28	24	23	18

4.4 THE GRADIENT OF A GRAPH

The **gradient** or **slope** of a graph (that is, how 'steep' the graph is,) measure the rate at which the 'y' variable is changing with respect to the 'x' variable.

The gradient is simply a change in the y value (denoted by Δy) divided by the corresponding change in the x value (denoted by Δx) as shown in Figure 4.12.

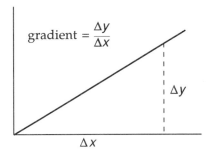

Figure 4.12

In Figure 4.13, the gradient is $6 \div 2 = 3$. Notice that in this graph the value of y is always 3 times the value of x; in other words, the equation of the line is $y = 3x$.

In general, the equation of a straight line through the origin is $y = mx$, where m is the gradient of the line. (See Section 4.1.)

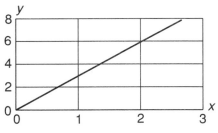

Figure 4.13

A graph such as that in Figure 4.14, which slopes in the opposite direction to that in the previous diagram, has a **negative** gradient. The gradient of this graph is -0.4

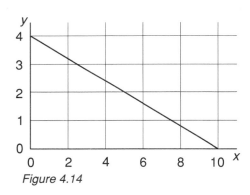

Figure 4.14

✍ *Student task 4.2*

What is the equation of the line shown in Figure 4.14?

(It will be of the form $y = mx + c$, since the line does not go through the origin. c is the intercept on the y-axis. See Pitfall 4.1.)

The gradient of a curved graph clearly changes - it is different at all points on the graph. In this case it is necessary to draw a tangent to the curve at the place in which you are interested, and find the gradient of that tangent, as shown in Figure 4.15.

The gradient of a graph often has a physical significance and can provide useful information about a situation. For example, the gradient of a graph of velocity against time is equal to the acceleration; the gradient of a graph of electric potential against distance is equal to the electric field.

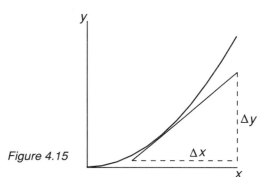

Figure 4.15

a) Calculate the gradients of the graphs shown in Figures 4.15 and 4.16.

b) Estimate the gradient of the graph in Figure 4.17 at point P and at point Q.

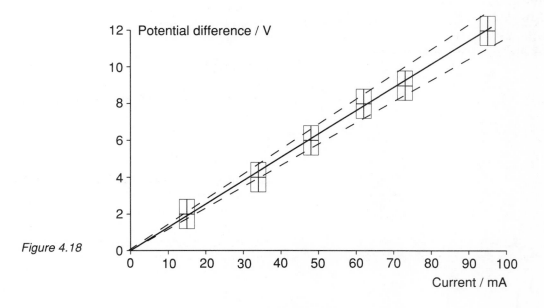

Figure 4.15   Figure 4.16

Figure 4.17

In Section 4.3 ('Drawing graphs') on page 31, the technique of using error bars to indicate the uncertainty of the measurements was introduced. The error bars define an 'error box', as shown in Figure 4.18. It follows that there must be some uncertainty over exactly where the line should go and hence some uncertainty over its gradient.

Figure 4.18 shows the same graph as Figure 4.11 from section 4.3. The two dashed lines show the two extremes for a graph which still passes through the error boxes associated with each of the points.

The gradient of the solid line is   12 V ÷ 95 mA = 126 Ω

The gradients of the two dotted lines are   13 V ÷ 95 mA = 137 Ω

and   11 V ÷ 95 mA = 116 Ω

Thus the uncertainty in the gradient is approximately ± 10 Ω, so we can write the resistance as determined by this graph is (126 ± 10) Ω (or 126 Ω ± 8%).

Figure 4.18

33

As well as the gradient of a graph which was dealt with in the last section, the 'area under a graph' can also give useful information about a physical situation.

The area under a graph is the area between the line of the graph and the x-axis, as shown in Figure 4.19.

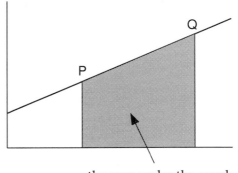

Figure 4.19   the area under the graph between points P and Q

Example

Figure 4.20 is a graph of force against extension for a spring. The area under this graph represents the work done on the spring (or the elastic potential energy stored in the spring). The work done on the spring when it is stretched by 10 cm is equal to the shaded area of the graph.

$$\therefore \text{ work done} = \tfrac{1}{2} \times 6\,\text{N} \times 0.1\,\text{m}$$

$$\text{work done} = 0.3\,\text{J}$$

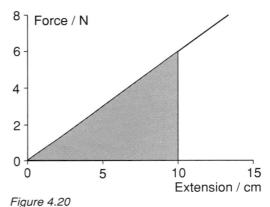

Figure 4.20

❋ Pitfall 4.2

Notice that the 'area under a graph' does not mean the *literal* area in square centimetres. (If it did, the area would depend on the scale you used for your graph!)

❋ Pitfall 4.3

Watch the units! In the example above, notice that the distance of 10 cm was converted to metres.

If the graph is a curve like Figure 4.21 rather than a straight line, then it is clearly more difficult to calculate the area, although it is usually possible to make a good approximation by dividing up the area under the graph into small sections and adding the area of each section.

In Figure 4.21 the area has been divided into two rectangles and two triangles. The triangles do not quite match the shape of the curve, so the total area calculated this way will be very slightly inaccurate.

An alternative method is to count the small squares on the graph paper.

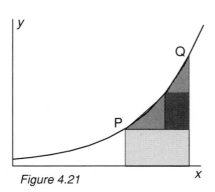

Figure 4.21

Example

Figure 4.22 shows a graph of force against extension for a rubber band. The area under the graph represents the work done in stretching the rubber band.

The area of one rectangular 'block', like the one that has been shaded, represents an energy of 0.5 N × 0.01 m = 0.005 J (5 mJ). The total number of rectangular 'blocks' under the graph is approximately 64 (using the method of counting squares), so the total energy represented by the area under the graph is 64 × 0.005 J = 0.32 J.

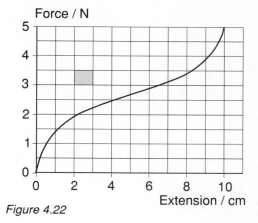

Figure 4.22

✍ *Student task 4.4*

Calculate the area under the graph in:

a) Figure 4.15, between x = 0 and x = 1.5

b) Figure 4.16, between x = 0 and x = 40

c) Figure 4.17, between x = 1 and x = 8

✍ *Student task 4.5*

Figure 4.23 shows a graph of speed against time for a train coming to rest at a station. The brakes are applied at time = 0 s. By measuring the area under the graph, estimate how far the train travels between first applying the brakes and coming to rest at the station. (Area under a speed - time graph = distance travelled.)

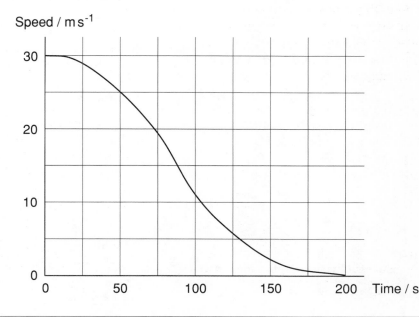

Figure 4.23

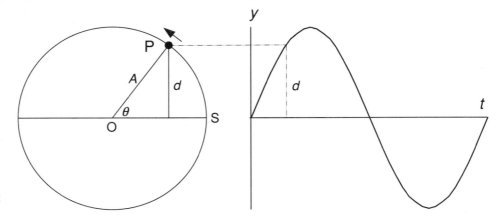

Figure 4.24

The equation for the sine curve shown in Figure 4.6 can be understood by relating to the motion of a particle moving round a circle.

Figure 4.24 represents a point P moving round a circle of radius A at constant speed, having started at S.

Next to the circle is a graph showing how the displacement d in the y direction varies with time.

From figure 4.24,

$$d = A \sin\theta$$

Since the point P is moving at constant speed, θ is proportional to time t, so a graph of y against t will be a sine curve as illustrated.

We can find the equation for this graph as follows. Assume θ is measured in radians (see Section 3.6).

If P takes a time T to complete a circle, this will be equal to the **period** of the oscillation. A complete circle contains 2π radians, so the time t for P to go from the start S to the position illustrated is given by

$$t = \frac{\theta}{2\pi} T$$

$$\therefore \theta = \frac{2\pi t}{T}$$

Substituting this value of θ into the equation for the displacement gives

$$d = A \sin \frac{2\pi t}{T}$$

The period $T = \frac{1}{f}$ where f = frequency

Thus the equation can also be written as

$$d = A \sin 2\pi f t$$

An alternative way of writing the equation is in terms of the **angular velocity** of P. The angular velocity is defined as the rate at which θ is increasing, and is usually denoted by the symbol ω. Hence

$$\omega = \frac{\theta}{t}$$

Therefore $\theta = \omega t$, and we can rewrite the equation for the curve as

$$d = A \sin \omega t$$

Comparison of the the two equations shows that $\omega = 2\pi f$. ω is sometimes referred to as the 'angular frequency' of the curve.

✍ Student task 4.6

a) The equation for a body moving with simple harmonic motion is given by:

$$y = 0.5 \sin 2t$$

i)   What is the amplitude of the oscillation?
ii) What is the frequency of the oscillation?
iii) What is the period of the oscillation?

b) A pendulum 0.8 m long swings with an amplitude of 0.2 m. Write an equation for its displacement as a function of time.

(First calculate the period of the pendulum using the standard equation.)

4.7 FITTING DATA TO A STRAIGHT LINE GRAPH

It is easy to check the shape of a straight line graph; all you need is a straight edge, such as a ruler. Physicists often choose to plot data in such a way as to yield a straight line graph.

If y is proportional to x^2, then a graph of y against x will give a parabola (see Section 4.2). However, a graph a y plotted against x^2 will yield a straight line passing through the origin. Similarly, if y is proportional to sine x, a graph of y against sine x will be a straight line through the origin.

Example

According to theory, the period of a simple pendulum is given by

$$T = 2\pi\sqrt{\frac{l}{g}}$$

Hence $T \propto \sqrt{l}$

An experiment was performed to see if this relationship held for a particular pendulum and the data shown in Table 4.1 was obtained.

Table 4.1

length / m	period / s
0.2	0.89
0.4	1.26
0.6	1.54
0.8	1.76
1.0	1.95
1.2	2.10
1.4	2.20
1.6	2.35

The graph shown in Figure 4.25 was drawn from this data, and its shape appears to be parabolic and hence confirm the relationship.

A graph of period against the square root of the length should yield a straight line. Figure 4.26 shows such a graph, the data having been calculated from Table 4.1 and tabulated in Table 4.2. It can be seen that the graph is not quite straight, showing that this pendulum did not in fact quite obey the expected relationship.

Without the straight line graph it would be very difficult to detect this departure from the expected relationship.

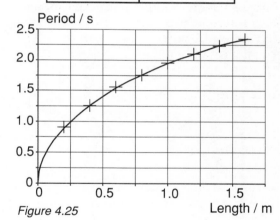

Figure 4.25

Figure 4.26

Table 4.2

√L / √m	period / s
0.45	0.89
0.63	1.26
0.77	1.54
0.89	1.76
1.00	1.95
1.10	2.10
1.18	2.20
1.26	2.35

It is not *essential* to know anything about calculus in order to understand A-level physics, but an appreciation of the basic ideas might help. The intention in this section is to cover the subject just sufficiently to enable the student to understand the basic ideas and the relevant notation.

i) Differentiation

In Physics we are often concerned with the rate at which one variable changes with respect to another. This is the gradient of the graph of the two variables, as discussed in Section 4.4. If the graph of the two variables is a straight line there is no difficulty in finding the gradient. If the graph is not a straight line, the gradient (and hence the rate of change) varies. Differentiation is concerned with finding the exact rate of change at any particular point on a graph. Differentiation would enable us to calculate the exact gradient of the tangent to the graph in Figure 4.15, provided we knew the equation of the curve.

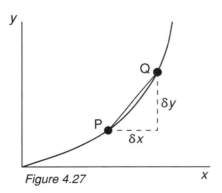

Figure 4.27

Look at Figure 4.27. The average gradient of the chord between P and Q is given by

$$\text{gradient} = \frac{\delta y}{\delta x}$$

If Q is very close to P, so that δx is very small, this average gradient will be very nearly equal to the gradient at P. The smaller δx becomes, the more nearly this average gradient is equal to the actual gradient. In mathematical language, we say that, in the limit, as δx approaches zero (that is, becomes

very small), the value of the average gradient becomes equal to the actual gradient at P. The mathematical notation for this precise gradient is $\frac{dy}{dx}$, and the mathematical notation for this last sentence is:

$$\frac{dy}{dx} = \frac{\delta y}{\delta x}_{\lim \delta x \to 0}$$

There are rules with which we can find the 'differential' of a function (that is, the rate at which y changes with respect to x). Three common differentials which might be met in A-level Physics are shown in Table 4.3.

Table 4.3

function	differential
$y = Ax^n$	$\frac{dy}{dx} = nAx^{n-1}$
$y = A\sin\omega t$	$\frac{dy}{dt} = \omega A\cos\omega t$
$y = A\cos\omega t$	$\frac{dy}{dt} = -\omega A\sin\omega t$

Example

If the equation of a curve is given by

$$y = 3x^2$$

then the differential is given by

$$\frac{dy}{dx} = 2 \times 3x = 6x$$

Therefore the gradient when $x = 4$ is 24.

✍ **Student task 4.7**

Find the gradient of the following:

a) $y = 4x^3$ when $x = 2$

b) $y = \frac{3}{x^2}$ when $x = 5$

   (Write this as $y = 3x^{-2}$.)

c) $y = 2\sqrt{x}$ when $x = 4$.

   (Write this as $y = 2x^{\frac{1}{2}}$.)

d) $y = 3\sin 2t$ when $t = 1\,\text{s}$

   (Remember ωt is in radians)

---

ii) Integration

Integration is concerned with finding the area under a graph. In Section 4.5 the problem of finding the area under a curved graph was discussed. In Figure 4.23 and Student Task 4.4, for example, it was necessary to divide the area into a number of rectangles and triangles, but this gives only an approximate value for the area.

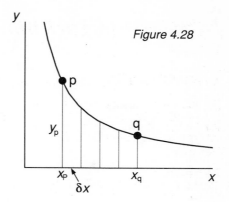

Figure 4.28

Figure 4.28 shows a curved graph. The area under the graph between P and Q can be divided into a number of strips, each of width δx. The area of the first strip is $y_P \, \delta x$; it is approximate because y_P is not constant across the width of the strip.

The total area under the graph between P and Q will be the sum of the areas of all the strips. In mathematical notation this is written as:

$$\text{Area} = \sum_{x_p}^{x_q} y\delta x$$

Σ is the greek letter 'sigma' and means 'the sum of'. The x_p and x_q written below and above the Σ indicate the starting and finishing values for x in the area under consideration, and are called the 'limits'.

The smaller the width of each strip, that is, as δx gets closer to zero, the more nearly will this approximate area be equal to the exact area under the graph.

The mathematical notation for this exact area is

$$\int_{x_p}^{x_q} y\mathrm{d}x$$

so we can write:

$$\text{Area} = \int_{x_p}^{x_q} y\mathrm{d}x = \sum_{x_p}^{x_q} y\delta x_{\text{lim } \delta x \to 0}$$

$\int$ is called the 'integral' sign.

Two integrals which might be encountered in A-level Physics are shown in Table 4.4. In this table, x_1 and x_2 are the limits of the integral, that is, the values of x between which the area is being calculated.

Table 4.4

function	integral
$y = Ax^n$	$\int_{x_1}^{x_2} y\mathrm{d}x = \left[\dfrac{Ax^{n+1}}{n+1}\right]_{x_1}^{x_2}$
$y = \dfrac{A}{x}$	$\int_{x_1}^{x_2} y\mathrm{d}x = \left[A\ln x\right]_{x_1}^{x_2}$

Example

The equation for a curve is $y = 6x^2$. What is the area under this curve between $x = 2$ and $x = 5$?

$$\text{Area} = \int_{2}^{5} y\mathrm{d}x$$

$$\text{Area} = \int_{2}^{5} 6x^2 \mathrm{d}x$$

Referring to Table 4.4, we must increase the power to which x is raised (the value of n) by 1, and divide by this new power. So the integral is equal to

$$\left(\frac{6x^3}{3}\right)_{2}^{5} = (2x^3)_{2}^{5}$$

If we substitute the *upper* limit into this equation, we find the area between $x = 0$ and $x = 5$; this area is $2 \times 5^3 = 250$ units. The area between $x = 0$ and the *lower* limit of $x = 2$ is $2 \times 2^3 = 16$ units. The difference between these two areas (250 - 16 = 234 units) is the area under the graph between $x = 2$ and $x = 5$.

39

5   *Logarithms and Exponentials*

5.1 INTRODUCTION

The mathematics in this chapter is likely to be new to most students, for it does not form part of National Curriculum key stage 4 or GCSE syllabuses. However, many changes in science are 'logarithmic' or 'exponential', and it is important to be able to understand the relevant mathematics.

5.2 WHAT IS A LOGARITHM?

$10^2 = 100$, or, in words, we raise 10 to the power 2 to obtain 100. The **logarithm** of 100 (to base 10) is therefore 2.

Similarly, $10^4 = 10\,000$, so logarithm to base 10 of 10 000 is 4. This would usually be written as

$$\log_{10} 10\,000 = 4, \text{ or } \log_{10} 10^4 = 4.$$

Usually, a logarithm, or 'log' for short, is not a whole number. For example,

$$\log_{10} 246 = 2.391, \text{ because } 10^{2.391} = 246.$$

A logarithm can be negative:

$$\log_{10} 0.01 = -2, \text{ because } 10^{-2} = 0.01$$
$$\log_{10} 0.45 = -0.347 \text{ because } 10^{-0.347} = 0.45$$

Notice also that

$$\log_{10} 1 = 0 \text{ because } 10^0 = 1$$

A logarithm does not have to have a base of 10. $4^3 = 64$, so log to base 4 of 64 is 3. This would be written as $\log_4 64 = 3$.

The logarithm of a number x is the power to which you must raise a base number in order to obtain the number x.

There are two common bases of logarithms. One of these bases is 10, as in the examples at the start of this section. If the base is not specified, the word 'log' (or 'lg') by itself implies the base is 10. For example, $\log 1000 = 3$ because $10^3 = 1000$; the base 10 is implied.

The other common base is 2.718 281 8.... - a number usually denoted by the letter e. The reason for such an apparently strange choice of base number is explained in section 5.7. Logarithms to the base e are denoted by the abbreviation ln (or sometimes $\log_e$). For example, $\ln 7.39 = 2$ because $e^2 = 7.39$.

A useful property of logarithms is

$$\log(a \times b) = \log a + \log b$$

5.3 LOGARITHMIC SCALES

Figure 5.1 is a bar chart showing the resistivities of various substances. Look at the scale on the y-axis. Each interval is *1000 times greater* than the previous interval. The y-axis *could* have been labelled 'log resistivity' with the numbers from -9 to +18.

A very large range of numbers can be represented conveniently by a **logarithmic scale** like this.

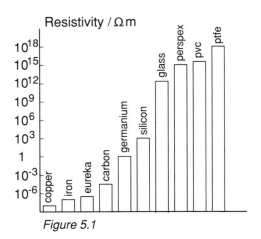

Figure 5.1

✍ **Student task 5.1**

How high would the bar for ptfe have to be if a conventional, linear, scale had been used for the y-axis in Figure 5.1, with 1 mm representing a resitivity of $10^{-8}\ \Omega$ m?

40

5.4 EXPONENTIAL GRAPHS

The table below contains a set of numbers showing how a variable y depends on x.

Table 5.1

x	0	1	2	3	4	5
y	1	2	4	8	16	32

Each value of y is twice the previous value. In other words, the ratio of any value of y divided by the previous value of y is always equal to 2 - it is constant.

A graph of y against x is shown below in Figure 5.2.

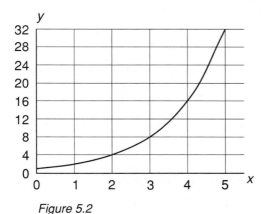

Figure 5.2

This shows a 'constant ratio' or **exponential** graph as introduced in Section 4.2.

The general equation for an exponential graph is $y = ka^x$, where k and a are constants.

k is the value of y when $x = 0$ (the 'starting point' of the graph).

a is the value of the constant ratio.

In this example the value of k is 1, and the value of a is 2, so the equation of this curve is:

$$y = 2^x.$$

✳ *Pitfall 5.1*

Notice that it is the ratio between pairs of y-values that is constant, **not** the ratio $y \div x$, which is the condition for direct proportionality (straight line graph through the origin.)

The table below shows another set of 'constant ratio' data, this time with the y-values decreasing.

Table 5.2

x	0	1	2	3	4	5
y	9	3	1	0.33	0.11	0.04

✍ *Student task 5.2*

What is the 'constant ratio' in this case?

A graph of y against x for these figures is shown below in Figure 5.3.

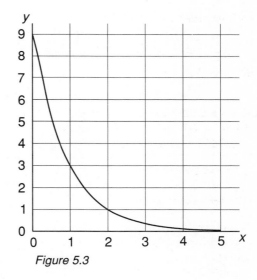

Figure 5.3

This is the shape of the 'exponential decay' curve associated with radioactive decay and the discharge of a capacitor.

The equation for this curve is

$$y = 9 \times \frac{1}{3^x} \quad \text{or} \quad 9 \times 3^{-x}$$

The general equation for an exponential decrease is therefore $y = ka^{-x}$.

41

5.5 A TEST FOR AN EXPONENTIAL GRAPH

Table 5.3 shows another set of 'constant ratio' data. In this case the ratio between successive values of y is 10, each value being 10 times greater than the previous one.

Table 5.3

x	0	1	2	3	4	5
y	10^2	10^3	10^4	10^5	10^6	10^7

The values for **log** y with the corresponding values for x are shown in Table 5.4.

Table 5.4

x	0	1	2	3	4	5
log y	2	3	4	5	6	7

Clearly log y increases linearly, so a graph of log y against x will be a straight line (not through the origin) as shown in Figure 5.4.

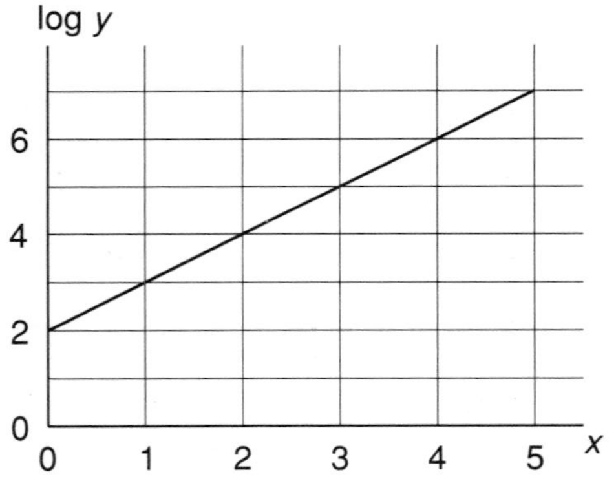

Figure 5.4

All exponential graphs give a straight line when log y is plotted against x. (Such a graph is sometimes called a 'semi-log' graph.) Logarithms to any base can be used - changing the base merely changes the gradient of the straight line graph.

The two tests for an exponential graph are:

1. Look for a constant ratio between successive values of y for constant increments of x.

2. Plot a graph of log y against x; a straight line indicates an exponential relationship.

> ❄ *Pitfall 5.2*
>
> Only the logarithm of the variable plotted on the y-axis (that is, the 'constant ratio' variable) is taken; the x variable remains unchanged.

> ✍ *Student task 5.3*
>
> Plot graphs of log y against x for the data shown in Tables 5.1 and 5.2 and show that these graphs are straight lines. (The data from Table 5.2 should give a negative slope.)

5.6 THE DISCHARGE OF A CAPACITOR

The discharge of a capacitor follows an exponential rule - a graph of charge on the capacitor against time is a 'constant ratio' one. This section looks in detail at why the graph is exponential, and what the exact equation of the graph is.

Consider a capacitor discharging through a resistor in a circuit such as shown in Figure 5.5.

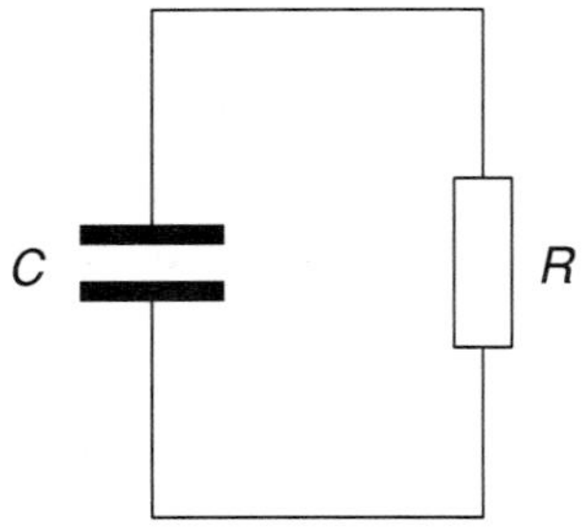

Figure 5.5

At a particular time t the charge left on the plates of the capacitor is Q, so the p.d. across the capacitor is Q/C. This p.d. drives a current I through the resistor. The value of the current is given by:

$$I = \frac{V}{R} = \frac{Q}{RC}$$

Suppose that in a small time interval Δt, the charge which flows from the capacitor is ΔQ. The current (which is charge ÷ time) is therefore given by:

$$I = \frac{-\Delta Q}{\Delta t}$$

The minus sign in front of the ΔQ indicates that the charge on the capacitor is **decreasing**.

Substituting for I in the first equation:

$$\frac{\Delta Q}{\Delta t} = \frac{-Q}{RC} \quad \text{or} \quad \frac{\Delta Q}{Q} = \frac{-\Delta t}{RC}$$

The charge which flows from the capacitor in the time interval Δt is proportional to the charge Q on the capacitor at that moment. In other words, in a given time interval, the same **fraction** of the charge which is on the capacitor at that time will always flow. The fraction which remains behind is always the same; in other words, the discharge follows the **constant ratio** or **exponential** rule.

A similar argument can be applied to the decay of a radioactive substance. The number of atoms which decay in a given time interval is proportional to the number of atoms present at that time, so radioactive decay also follows an exponential decrease.

In general, **exponential changes arise whenever the rate of change of a quantity** (that is, the amount by which it changes in a given time interval) **is proportional to the quantity itself.**

In mathematical notation:

$$\frac{\Delta y}{\Delta t} \propto y$$

Since the discharge follows an exponential pattern, from Section 5.4 the equation for the discharge curve must be of the form

$$Q = Q_0 a^{-t}$$

However, this is always written as

$$Q = Q_0 e^{-t/RC}$$

where $a = e^{1/RC}$ and is the 'constant ratio' between successive Q values as t increases by 1.

Why should the solution be written in this form?

In general, we are looking for a solution to an equation of the form

$$\frac{dy}{dt} = ky$$

that is, the differential of the function is equal to the function itself multiplied by a constant.

Suppose, for simplicity, that $k = 1$. A function of the form

$$y = y_0\left(1 + t + \frac{t^2}{2!} + \frac{t^3}{3!} + \dots\right)$$

satisfies this condition.

($n!$ means $n(n-1)(n-2)\dots3\times2\times1$, so, for example. $3!$ means $3\times2\times1=6$. The ! symbol is called 'factorial'.)

The function

$$\left(1 + t + \frac{t^2}{2!} + \frac{t^3}{3!} + \dots\right)$$

is called the **exponential** function. When differentiated term by term we obtain

$$\frac{dy}{dt} = y_0\left(0 + 1 + t + \frac{t^2}{2!} + \dots\right)$$

But $y_0\left(0 + 1 + t + \frac{t^2}{2!} + \dots\right)$

is the same as the original function y. Hence

$$\frac{dy}{dt} = y$$

The exponential function is written as e^t, so the solution can be written as:

$$y = y_0 e^t$$

More generally,

$$\text{if } \frac{dy}{dt} = ky \text{ then } y = y_0 e^{kt}$$

In the case of the capacitor, the constant k is equal to $-1/RC$, so the charge Q at any instant t is given by

$$Q = Q_0 e^{-t/RC}.$$

5.7 NATURAL LOGARITHMS

The base of natural logarithms is the number e, which, from above, is equal to

$$1 + \frac{1}{1!} + \frac{1}{2!} + \frac{1}{3!} + \ldots = 2.718 \ldots$$

As first explained in Section 5.2, the natural logarithm of a number is the power to which e must be raised in order to equal that number.

If $y = e^t$, then $t = \ln y$ by the above definition, so a graph of $\ln y$ against t will give a straight line (see Section 5.5).

5.8 LOG-LOG GRAPHS

Look at the graph in Figure 5.6. This could be a graph showing that y is proportional to x^2, or perhaps y is proportional to x^3, or something else of the form y proportional to x^n, where n is a constant.

If we have a good idea what the relationship is (because we know the relevant theory, perhaps,) then we can draw a graph of y against x^n, expecting to obtain a straight line as explained in Section 4.7.

However, if we have no idea of the correct value for n, we can determine its value by plotting a graph of $\log y$ against $\log x$.

Suppose the equation of the curve is of the form $y = Ax^n$, where A and n are constants. Taking logs of both sides of the equation gives

$$\log y = \log Ax^n$$

Since $\log (C \times D) = \log C + \log D$ (see Section 5.2) this can be written as:

$$\log y = \log x^n + \log A$$
$$\log y = n \log x + \log A$$

This is of the form

$$Y = mX + C$$

which is the equation of a straight line, gradient m and intercept on the Y axis of C.

Hence the equation of $\log y$ against $\log x$ will give a straight line of gradient n and intercept on the $\log y$ axis of $\log A$, as in Figure 5.7. Hence both n and A can be determined in the equation for the curve.

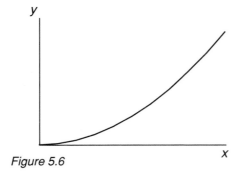

Figure 5.6

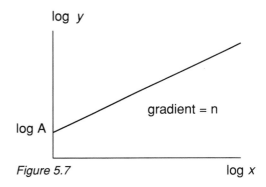

Figure 5.7

Answers to Student Tasks

1.1 a) i) y^{13}
      ii) y^{12}
      iii) y^3
      iv) $12y^5$

   b) i) 81
      ii) 2
      iii) 0.04
      iv) 27
      v) 0.25
      vi) 1

1.2 a) $u = v - at$
   b) $E_k = hf - \varphi$
   c) $\dfrac{1}{v} = \dfrac{1}{f} - \dfrac{1}{u}$

1.3 a) $B = \dfrac{F}{Il}$
   b) $\rho = \dfrac{RA}{l}$
   c) $V = \dfrac{Q}{C}$

1.4 a) $l = \dfrac{RA}{\rho}$
   b) $x = \dfrac{\lambda l}{s}$
   c) $v = \sqrt{\dfrac{Fr}{m}}$
   d) $r = \sqrt{\dfrac{Gm_1 m_2}{F}}$
   e) $E = \rho c^2$
   f) $T = \mu\left(\dfrac{f}{2\pi}\right)^2$
   g) $L = \dfrac{1}{C(2\pi f_r)^2}$

1.5 b) If the ball had been thrown up from the ground so that it rose past the top of the tower, it would have come down again, passing the top of the tower at 15 m/s, 5.3 s after leaving the ground.

1.6 The resistance halves.

2.1 a) $(6 + 5) \times (3 + 7)$
   b) $6 + 5 \times (3 + 7)$
   c) $(6 + 5) \times 3 + 7$

2.2 $(2 + 4 \times 3) \div 7 =$

2.3 $(2 \times 10) \div (5 \times 3) =$

2.4 a) 3.47×10^3
   b) 6.8×10^7
   c) 2.7×10
   d) 5.94×10^{-1}
   e) 9.2×10^{-4}
   f) 2.642×10^2

2.5 a) 5.89 EXP 24
   b) 6.36 EXP 6
   c) 1.6 EXP $\pm$ 19
   d) 6.63 EXP $\pm$ 34

2.6 -

2.7 a) 7.21×10^{-6} V
   b) 4.2×10^{10} W
   c) 3.9×10^{-10} F
   d) 5.92×10^8 J
   e) 1.9×10^{-14} A

2.8 $375\,\Omega$

2.9 $(5.3 \pm 0.4) \times 10^3$ m/s

2.10 8.0×10^3 m/s

3.1 a) i) $27°$
      ii) 6.7 cm
      iii) 9 cm^2
   b) i) $53°$
      ii) 4.5 cm
      iii) 13.5 cm^2
   c) i) $50°$
      ii) 5.0 cm
      iii) 10.5 cm^2

3.2 a) 0.156
   b) 0.754
   c) 0.914

3.3 a) $18.7°$
   b) $74.3°$
   c) $58.2°$

3.4 -

3.5 a) 5.7 cm
   b) 8.2 cm
   c) $31°$
   d) 58.3 cm
   e) 6.1 cm
   f) 9.7 cm
   j) $7.2°$
   k) 7.9 cm

3.6 -

3.7 a) 11.7 m/s, $31°$
   b) 0.54 N/C, $22°$
   c) 6.9 N, $30°$

3.8 $V_E = 4.6$ m/s
    $V_S = 3.9$ m/s

3.9 $T = 2.2$ N

3.10 a) i) 0.35 rad
      ii) 1.31 rad
      iii) 1.57 rad $(\pi/2)$
    b) i) $22.9°$
      ii) $43°$
      iii) $91.7°$
    c) 0.22 rad
    d) 7.2 cm

3.11 The explanation is plausible; the angular separation of the edges of Venus is about 10^{-4} rad, which is about the same as the angular resolution of the eye.

4.1 -

4.2 $y = -0.4x + 4$ or $5y + 2x = 20$

4.3 a) Fig. 4.15: 8
      Fig. 4.16: -0.125
   b) P: about 5
      Q: about 0.5

4.4 a) 9.8
   b) 100
   c) about 15

4.5 2.7 km

4.6 a) i) 0.5 m
      ii) 0.3 Hz
      iii) 3.1 s $(\pi$ s)
   b) $y = 0.2 \sin 3.5t$

4.7 a) 48
   b) -0.048
   c) 0.5
   d) -2.5

5.1 10^{23} m. (About 10^7 light years - 100 times the diameter of our galaxy!)

5.2 0.33

5.3 -